Tap Into Your Healing Power

By Becca Pronchick

ISBNs:

Print: 978-1-64184-193-1

ebook: 978-1-64184-169-6

Table of Contents

Part 2 - Physical Healing

Part 3 - Emotional Healing

Part 4 - Try It On Everything

Part 5 - Additional Information & Techniques

Part 6 - Self-Care

Introduction

My journey first took me from Hollywood, California to Garden Grove, California where I was raised by two actors who never made it into show business, except in community theater. My father had dozens of jobs over the years, lived with chronic pain that he medicated with alcohol and made life miserable for everyone around him. My mother worked as a secretary in the 1950s and 1960s, when women didn't work outside the home very much. She was loving, kind, and wise. However, she suffered deeply from depression and debilitating illness. My saving grace was my mother's mother who lovingly raised my younger brother and I when my mother worked and later when she stayed in bed.

I left home the day I turned 18 and launched myself into the world with my intelligence and an ability to type, but with virtually no social or survival skills. Two marriages and a number of administrative jobs brought me to the age of 30, terrified and longing for the meaning of my life.

While employed at a large university I began to study photography at night and embarked on my second career as a professional photographer. I was a very successful entrepreneur and a crazy workaholic for the next 15 years. Fortunately I met husband number three, my last husband, who has been the love of my life for over 34 years.

In my late 40s, I experienced my first, or perhaps second, breakdown when I could no longer lift my arms. Physical therapy, rest, yoga and meditation helped me heal and also guided me to study as a yoga and meditation instructor. Two years later I was a certified wellness coach and teacher, my third and final career.

I learned about Emotional Freedom Techniques (EFT) in a very painful way. In 2006 I had one of those years with one loss after another and by 2007 I was in horrible pain in my lower back and wasn't sure what was wrong.

While I was in the certification process to become a life coach, I hired a wonderful young coach who was ahead of me in the training and I loved working with her. She was challenging me to be courageous about building my own coaching business and we were just beginning to offer events together. Then, in April of 2006, she died very suddenly at the age of 42.

In June my step-mother, who was 87 years young and had been living near us for many years after my father died, went into the hospital and was told there was nothing they could do to help her. I went day after day to the hospital to see her and talk with her doctor. Finally I brought her home to Napa and called in hospice. She was so loving and gracious through the entire process. The hospice team was wonderful at taking care of her in her retirement home. She and I got along well and I was so grateful to be close to her. We invited her favorite nephew to visit and the last time I saw her we said goodbye and she said she was ready to go. I facilitated a touching and meaningful memorial service for her friends and my husband took care of all of her affairs, including sending her precious belongings to her family.

Our dear cat, Burt, who had been with us for 18 years, was declining at the same time, so I had asked Burt if he could please wait a little while and he agreed. He really did. He waited and then he died peacefully at home in August. We really grieved and realized that we had one more loss to process.

By November of that year I began to have horrible, stabbing pains in my lower back. It was months before I was able to see my doctor. He requested an MRI and then told me "it's really bad and it's not going to get any better." I was diagnosed with severe degenerative disc disease and osteoarthritis. He prescribed pain medication and referred me to physical therapy.

I agreed to begin physical therapy and trusted my intuition to not to take the medication. I attended weekly physical therapy and acupuncture sessions and rested on an ice pack on my couch for six months. Then I was referred to a naturopath for help with chronic pain. She said "have you heard of this crazy tapping thing?" My friends had been telling me about EFT and had even given me a large, photocopied manual from Gary Craig, the founder of EFT.

This technique is truly the key to healing – physically, emotionally, mentally and spiritually.

Gary is an engineer and the huge manual hadn't made sense to me. The naturopath, however, said, "let me show you how to tap and then you can go home and practice." She spent about 10 minutes showing me the basic tapping technique and I went home and practiced every day. What else was I going to do? I couldn't sit, couldn't drive, couldn't teach. I was motivated!!

After two weeks of tapping – literally all I knew to say was, "All this pain," "all this pain," "all this pain in my lower back" – the pain went away! Honest truth. The pain was gone. My body still lets me know when I sit too long and periodically flares up. However, I'm able to recover very quickly, thank goodness.

I was so amazed, delighted and impressed with this "crazy tapping thing" that I had to find somewhere to learn more and share it with my clients. I found a teacher nearby and launched myself into training as an EFT practitioner. I continued for two years until I became an EFT Master trainer and started teaching the technique right away. I have never looked back and have continued to experience so many healings personally and professionally in all of the years since.

This book is dedicated to all of you who give yourself permission to be healthy, strong, powerful, passionate, compassionate and wise. I wanted to pull together many of the lessons I have created over the years and inspire you to step into health and wellbeing for yourself, your family and friends and for all beings. From my heart to yours with many blessings.

PART 1

The Basics

EFT Basic Recipe

Link to Basic Recipe video:
https://www.youtube.com/
uiEjPI&list=PL6sc__uV8x9byWOnZYY-4aSYFdmcEHVNM

What is Emotional Freedom Technique (EFT)?

Tapping technique is providing thousands of people with relief from pain, diseases and emotional issues. Simply stated, it is a unique version of acupuncture except you don't use needles. Instead, you **stimulate well established energy meridian points on your body by tapping them with your fingertips, while *psychologically tuning in* to an issue.** The process is easy to learn and can be practiced by anyone.

After thousands of years of studying our body's energy pathways, we now know that imbalances, or blockages, in the flow of energy can result in both emotional and physical difficulties. This idea has been largely ignored by Western healing practices and we now see that this is why tapping often works where nothing else will.

There are many different types of Energy Therapies out there (Acupuncture, Reiki, Polarity to name a few) and tapping the meridian points is unique in that it is an Energy Psychology. It combines the gentle tapping of acupressure points with the psychological "tuning in" to the problem. Here's how it's done.

The Basic Recipe

The Set Up statement – Choose the condition or issue you would like to address.

1. Write down your set up statement and focus on the sensation in your body as you are tapping.
2. Measure the intensity of the condition or issue as it exists now while you are tuning in.
3. Rate the intensity on a scale of 1 to 10 to begin.
4. While tapping on the side of both hands at the base of the little fingers, say the set up statement three times. For example: "Even though I have this pain, I totally and completely love, accept and forgive myself, and I am safe."
5. Keep your eyes open and speak the Set Up statement out loud.

The Tapping Sequence & Reminder Statement – Tap each of the points on the face, chest, under the arms, ribs, inside the wrists and crown of the head 5 – 7 times while repeating the

Reminder Statement. For example: "This pain, this pain, this pain in my knee." Repeat this sequence three times.

TAPPING POINTS

Here are the tapping points:

1. Eyebrows – at the beginning of the eyebrow, just above the nose.
2. Side of the eyes – on the bone bordering the outside of the eye.
3. Cheekbones – on the cheek bone directly under the eye.
4. Under the nose – in the center of the area between the nose and top lip.
5. Chin – in the center on the chin.
6. Chest – just below the collar bones on both sides.
7. Under the arms – on the sides of the body down from the armpits.
8. Lower ribs – just below the breasts.

9. Inside both wrists palms facing so fingertips tap inside both wrists.

10. Crown of the head – toward the back of the head, just before it goes vertical. This is where many of the energy channels come together.

Testing the Results

1. Measure your progress by observing the level of intensity and note the change. If the issue is less severe, but still noticeable, change the Set-Up Statement to something like this:

"*Even though I still have some remaining pain, I totally and completely love, accept and forgive myself.*"

2. Then repeat the Tapping Sequence, alternating on the points, with an altered Reminder Statement such as:

"*This remaining pain, I'd really like to let this go, this remaining pain, it's time to relax and let go, this remaining pain, it's safe to release and let go, this remaining pain, I'm ready to relax and open to the healing.*"

3. Keep repeating this process until the intensity of the issue has dropped below a 2 or 3 in intensity. When there is very little pain remaining, tap one more time around with the statement:

"*I now choose to fully overcome this issue, and I totally and completely love and accept myself.*"

What to do when it appears not to be working:

1. Drink plenty of water before, during and after practicing.

2. Be persistent - continue to practice every day until the issue begins to diminish. Even a few minutes of tapping can be very effective.
3. Be specific – continue to fine tune your set-up statement.
4. Expect hidden or shifting aspects – allow the process to unfold and keep going with the tapping.
5. Remove watches, jewelry, tight clothing or anything that might interfere with the process.
6. Practice while undisturbed – turn off the cell phone, TV or music.

Link To EFT Tapping Video: https://www.youtube.com/watch?v=QB286uiEjPI

Remember to tap every day even when you begin to feel better. Enjoy!

Benefits of EFT Tapping Practice

Pain relief, stress relief, relaxation and peace of mind are some of the many benefits of EFT tapping. Tapping activates acupressure points on your face and upper body, while calming your nervous system, calming the primitive brain, calming the stress response and moving energy throughout your body. I believe there is also a great benefit in acknowledging whatever is happening and then beginning to release and let go.

When we are in pain, anxious or stressed we have a tendency to ignore the symptoms, distract ourselves and push through. Eventually the circumstances persist and then we are forced to slow down and pay attention. Daily practice allows us to pay better attention and address the issues before they become severe.

One big benefit of EFT tapping practice is to relieve symptoms and conditions without resorting to medication or other treatment. Always consult your doctor when necessary and see how your self-care can help with the emotional impact and anxiety.

Tapping Points

When I originally trained in EFT, I was taught 8 tapping points, not including the ribs and wrists. Then I began to study with an acupuncturist who now teaches and practices EFT exclusively. She added the wrist points and the rib points, which are liver points, good for releasing anger and fear.

There is no particular order to the tapping points. I tend to begin with the eyebrow points and end with the top of the head. I like to take a deep breath at the chest and at the top of the head.

Many of my clients find their favorite points and hang out there. I'm also very fond of patting the heart and saying, "there, there" to my body and my mind for comfort and ease.

One Hand or Two When Tapping?

When I started training we were taught to tap with only one hand, as many other EFT teachers and practitioners still do. Then when I studied with the acupuncturist, she suggested tapping with both hands. It does work just as well tapping with only one hand.

Set Up Statements

Once you have chosen the topic for your tapping session, you are ready to craft your Set Up Statement. Basically this is a phrase that helps you to focus the session. Here's the structure of a Set Up Statement:

"Even though I have/feel/think ________________ (fill in the blank) with a symptom, emotion or condition.

Part of me might be holding on, for whatever reason, conscious or unconscious. ***For a psychological reversal, more about that soon.***

I acknowledge these feelings – this frustration, pain, sadness, etc.

I'm listening to my body, I'm telling the truth, I'm allowing the energy to move.

I now choose to relax and let go of this _____________.

I'm open to the healing. My body knows how to heal.

I love and accept myself, just as I am."

For example:

"Even though I have this nasty pain and part of me is holding on, consciously or unconsciously, I acknowledge these feelings and allow the energy to move. I now choose to relax and let go of the pain and open to the healing with love and acceptance."

It is not critical what you say. Most importantly you want to focus on the physical sensations and the emotions. You don't even need to say anything or create a Set Up statement. Try centering yourself, checking in with your body and mind and then simply tapping around on the body points.

At first, if saying "I love and accept myself" is difficult, try saying, "I'm OK." Or, "I'm open and receptive." Or, "I honor myself and all my feelings."

You will undoubtedly receive the healing benefits of relaxation, greater ease and calm, clarity, stress relief and most often more information about how to respond to your situation.

Psychological Reversals in Set-Up Statements

This is another innovation from my master EFT teacher, Lindsay Kinney. Reversals stem from our very natural and helpful resistance to change. The resistance is a survival mechanism and often a hindrance to healing. Even when we feel lousy, we may resist asking for help, changing our beliefs and behaviors or even admitting how much the issue is impacting the quality of our lives.

In the Set Up statement, it is very helpful to acknowledge the part of you that is holding on – for whatever reason. We may or may not be aware of the resistance and fortunately it doesn't matter. There may be a down side to getting better or releasing the past. We might be so familiar with feeling bad that we can't imagine who we will be without those feelings. Perhaps we have settled for feeling bad for so long, that it's inconceivable to us to feel better.

When you begin to tap on your issue, more insight and information will most likely arise. You might even say, "even though I'm not ready to let this go, I accept myself and all my feelings." Come back another time or another day to address this issue again. Be gentle with yourself.

You might also say, "*I've been feeling this way for so long and I'm willing to begin to consider letting it go*." This phrase always makes me laugh. You might tap and say, "*can't let this go – you can't make me*!" I find that it's always helpful to bring humor into the practice.

Why Combine Meditation & Tapping?

Link to Preparation for Meditation video:
https://www.youtube.com/watch?v=dNp-hKkzgFE&t=153s

When I learned EFT I was already a yoga and meditation instructor and had been practicing meditation daily for over ten years. It felt natural to me to add the tapping to my daily meditation practice and when I began to teach EFT, it made perfect sense to guide my clients into a meditative place to check in with their body, to quiet their mind and to center in a space of awareness and healing.

If you are not interested or not able to meditate, you might think of this as awareness practice. Especially when you are not feeling well physically it can be extremely helpful to slow down, get centered and listen to your body for guidance and connection.

Can't Quiet Your Mind?

First of all, I practice all of the techniques and practices that I teach. I'm not just regurgitating something I read in a book or on-line. I began to study Meditation in the early 1980's and, for many years, didn't have a daily spiritual practice.

Routine, environment, energization exercises, yoga postures, breathing practices, mantra and progressive relaxation are all methods to quiet the mind and body and prepare for meditation.

Then in the late 1990's I trained at The Expanding Light at Ananda in Nevada City, California as an Ananda Yoga & Meditation instructor and began to practice and understand the benefits of daily practice.

If you are struggling with settling down to meditate, finding the time to meditate or quieting your mind when you do decide to meditate - I know exactly how you feel. It can be frustrating, discouraging and not fun to feel that you don't know how to meditate and you don't understand why so many people practice and enjoy the benefits and, for some reason, you can't seem to get it. Here are some helpful guidelines.

Link to EFT Tapping Video:
https://www.youtube.com/watch?v=n_qlbCxDTXA

Neutralizing the Unconscious Resistance to Change

When we are aware of some resistance to what we desire, or even when we are not aware of the specifics, we can use Neutralizing to clear the way for the conditions and circumstances we desire.

While tapping on the karate chop point, try a statement such as: *"Even though I don't really want to let this go, for whatever reason, conscious or unconscious, I totally and completely love and accept myself."* Repeat three times, then move on to the Basic Recipe.

Choosing Your Topic for Practice

The best way to begin your EFT tapping practice session is to get settled and centered and bring your awareness down into your body. You might focus your session on a physical symptom, such as pain, tension, stress or stiffness. Headaches are especially responsive to tapping. You can expect results in just a few minutes. I've even had clients tell me that tapping has cleared their migraine headaches. Amazing!

Tapping is also very effective when you focus on a chronic condition, such as arthritis or fatigue. You might write down your Set Up statement or simply focus your awareness on your topic. It can be helpful to include the emotions you are feeling as well, such as frustration, confusion or anger. For example: *"Even though I am so frustrated about this diagnosis/condition/symptom and part of me is holding on, for whatever reason. I acknowledge these feelings, allowing the energy to move and I now choose to relax, let go and open to the healing with love and acceptance."*

As you are tapping you may receive more information and clarity about your condition. On the next round you can include the new information, acknowledge the resistance to change.

For example:

"*Even though I feel so much resistance to letting this go, I accept myself and all my feelings. All this resistance…all this resistance… can't seem to let this go…not ready to let this go. I'd really like to let this go.*"

Often, when we are willing to begin tapping and move the energy, we fairly quickly gain more information and begin to feel relief from the intense emotions. Remember to be gentle with yourself. It most likely took some time for you to develop this condition or symptom and it will take some time for you to release it.

Acute symptoms, such as headaches, are usually relieved quite quickly, thank goodness. More complex issues can take longer to resolve. The key to effective healing and relief is consistent practice with patience and persistence.

Tap Until You Feel Relief

It is important to know that with complex issues such as chronic pain, weight loss or anxiety, the healing may take a longer time. At each session it is helpful to tap until you begin to feel relief and the intensity is coming down. Then you will do another tapping round to alternate what you say on the points and begin to include Releasing Statements. For example: *"Even though I feel more relaxed, part of me might still be holding on. I now choose to relax and let go of this pain/condition/symptom with love and acceptance." "This remaining pain, it's time to let it go… this remaining pain, I'm relaxing and letting go…this remaining pain, it's safe to release and let go…this remaining pain, feeling so much better now."*

Once you feel more comfortable, open and relaxed, you can complete your practice with a positive or gratitude round. *"I'm so grateful for the healing…feeling more relaxed… listening to my body…I am calm, I am open and receptive…Feeling strong and grounded."*

Checking In Between Rounds of Tapping

Even in brief tapping sessions, it is good to pause between rounds and check in with your body and your emotions. Tap around on the body points, breathe for one or two rounds and then stop and rest. Notice your thoughts, emotions and physical sensations. What do you notice? Listen to your inner critic. Has the intensity of your emotions increased, decreased or stayed the same? Have the physical sensations changed or moved? All of these are possible and to be expected.

If the intensity has increased or stayed the same, continue tapping. You might alter what you are saying or simply continue to tap and breathe. When the intensity begins to come down, you are ready for your Releasing round and then your Positive or Gratitude round. Also, remember to be gentle with yourself. Rest, drink plenty of water and come back to the practice at another time, later or on another day.

Intensity Levels – SUDs

SUDs stands for Subjective Unit of Distress. Many EFT practitioners utilize the SUDs level to access results of the practice. When you choose your topic and begin the practice, you might notice the level of intensity, on a scale of 0 to 10, with 0 being no discomfort and 10 being the highest level of discomfort. Then you may check your SUDs level when you check in between rounds, and continue tapping until the level is down to a 1 or 2 before you begin your Releasing round.

Simple vs Complex Issues

We have already spoken about simple vs complex issues with tapping. Simple issues are acute pain like a headache, feeling nervous about an upcoming appointment, waking up after a less than satisfying night of sleep and feeling tired. Simple, current issues are very responsive to tapping and can clear quite quickly.

Complex issues are chronic pain, anxiety, weight loss or quitting smoking. These issues are long standing, more complicated and can take longer to resolve. Being patient and gentle with yourself will eventually offer relief and clarity. Your willingness to change is really the key to healing in these situations. You may also find that as you practice with these issues, you will gain more clarity and guidance about your conditions and your feelings about them.

This can be a good time to work with an EFT practitioner who will support you and work through your issues with you by asking powerful questions and utilizing intuition to strategize and explore what might have been happening in your life when this issue arose. There are often a number of emotional as well as physical aspects to our more challenging conditions.

EFT Shortcuts

When you are not inclined to sit down for a full EFT tapping session, I highly recommend some EFT shortcuts. Shortcuts are also great fun to practice throughout the day – when stopping at a red light in the car, in a meeting or when you only have a few minutes to center yourself and calm down.

Patting your heart and taking a slow, deep breath can be very calming to bring your awareness back to the present moment.

Tapping your fingertips together also activates the energy flow throughout your body and can be an unobtrusive way to tap in public.

You might even just imagine that you are tapping when you would like to calm yourself down, because your body will respond to what you are imagining.

Touch & Breathe

Link to Touch & Breathe video: https://www.youtube.com/watch?v=YZHO6TI6HlY

This is a very gentle and simple way to heal a headache and clear congestion. Rather than tapping on the points on the face, you simply touch the inner eyebrow points and breathe, then touch the temples and breathe, then touch the cheekbones and breathe. Continue touching and breathing on those three points until you feel relief of the headache or congestion.

PART 2

Physical Healing

Acupressure Technique for Respiratory Health

1. Settle yourself down for a few minutes of gentle self-care.
2. Press up under the inside of your eyebrows with your thumbs. There is a small notch there - gently press or rub those points and breathe...
3. Massage the temples on both sides and breathe...
4. Press index fingers into the notch on either side at the base of the nose. There is also a small notch there. Breathe...
5. Massage where the jaw connects in front of both ears. Breathe...
6. Gently run your finger tips from up under the ear lobes, down the throat to the collar bones on both sides - two or three times.

7. With the fingers of the right hand, gently rub inside the left shoulder for a few breaths. Repeat on the right side with left fingers.
8. Hold the web between the thumb and index finger on the left hand with the thumb and index finger of the right hand, thumb on top. Press or gently rub that point. Repeat on the right hand.
9. With left arm relaxed across the belly hold the left elbow with the right hand, thumb on top, just inside the bend. Repeat on the right.

Enjoy the ease of breathing throughout the day!

Restful Sleep & Sweet Dreams

- Are you having trouble sleeping sufficiently?
- Is lack of sleep affecting your quality of life?
- Does grumpiness get in the way of your JOY?

I hear you! So many of my clients express their difficulty with sleep - either getting to sleep or getting to sleep and then waking up and not being able to get back to sleep.

Here are several suggestions to improve the quality and quantity of your sleep - leading to peaceful rest and sweet dreams.

1. A**cupuncture or EFT Tapping** - Multiple clinical studies found that acupuncture may provide relief for insomnia. This technique involves inserting and manipulating thread-like needles into hundreds of "acupuncture points" on the body. Or simply tapping around on the body points will relax and calm your body and mind.

2. **Turn Off the TV** - To improve your sleep, you might consider improving your sleep environment. Clear your bedroom of your TV or other distractions, including computers, work materials, and any noises and bright lights. Research also suggests that TVs and computers generate electromagnetic fields (EMFs) that may disrupt the pineal gland, the source of the hormone melatonin, which regulates the body's circadian rhythms responsible for maintaining sleep cycles.
3. **Replace Worn-Out Pillows and Mattresses** - I recently realized that I can't remember the last time I replaced my pillow. My husband and I enjoy our Tempurpedic mattress and it's such a delight to sleep on new sheets and pillow cases.
4. For an all-natural energy-booster, try taking a vitamin B-12 supplement. A study published in the British Journal of Nutrition shows that this antioxidant is vital for energy production. B12 may also help to metabolize carbohydrates, fat and proteins, and promote healthy growth, cardiovascular and neurological health.
5. **Listen to relaxing music** - Listening to relaxing music signals your mind and body that it's time to slow down and sleep. A Journal of Advanced Nursing study found that soothing music had a very positive effect on the sleeping habits of adults.
6. **Bedtime routine is important**. Your brain and body need to unwind before sleep can occur. That's why you need to establish bedtime "rituals." Take a bath, meditate, do some easy stretches or yoga -- anything that lets the stress and chaos of the day melt away.

Perform your routine in the same way, in the same place, and at the same time each night. This repetition triggers your mind and body that it's time to relax and sleep.

Also eliminate negative activities or items, which are associated with sleeplessness. For example, if looking at a bedroom clock makes you anxious about how long you have until you need to get up, move the clock out of sight.

7. **Stimulus-Control Therapy** for insomnia:

Go to bed only when sleepy.

- Allow yourself 15 - 20 minutes to fall asleep.
- If not asleep within 15 - 20 minutes, get out of bed, go to another room, and engage in a calming activity (such as reading) until you feel sleepy.
- Repeat steps 1 - 3 as often as necessary.
- Get up at the same time each morning, even if you had a difficult night.

8. **If All Else Fails** - One of my favorite natural remedies is Bach Flower Essences. I've used Rescue Remedy for years and they also have Rescue Sleep. Both are available at your local pharmacy.

Reducing Inflammation

More and more we are learning that stress causes inflammation and that inflammation causes illness.

What irritates you?
What are you doing that you don't want to do?
Are your joints inflamed? How about your skin?

We each have our unique ways of responding to stress. I'm beginning to accept that my body is telling me something important when I don't feel well.

It can begin with a simple annoyance - The garage door opener isn't working. So I call the repair person. The repair person doesn't return my call. I'm more impatient - I want this puppy repaired - now!

This item stays on my to-do list day after day and adds to my stress level. I'm tense, I'm tired and grumpy. Know the feeling?

The garage door opener will get repaired, eventually. However, when several of these items pile up, we are responding to the world with irritation and our bodies are responding with inflammation.

I am suggesting for you to set aside some quiet time, perhaps with your journal, get settled and meditate for a few minutes.

Be honest with yourself as you write. Allow yourself to relax more and more and open to your inner wisdom and guidance.

Ask yourself - what am I doing that I don't want to do? Have I agreed to activities that I no longer enjoy? Am I pushing myself to please others?

I'm reminded of our frequent return to the Visioning Guided Meditation (found on page 90) , where we ask "What is the Vision?" "What am I Releasing to fulfill this Vision?"

Perhaps your irritation and subsequent inflammation in your body can be relieved by trusting what you are guided to release.

Remember to tap on the emotions, the physical sensations and the thoughts that are limiting your experience of ease and enjoyment. Keep tapping until you feel relief.

Physical & Emotional Impact of Pain

"Tapping is so effective at relieving chronic pain because it helps release unresolved emotions keeping the body in a stressed-out state. By tapping to remove the negative emotional charge from specific events and other past and current issues, the brain gets the message that it is safe to relax tense muscles and lessens nerve sensitivity. That's when the body can heal itself of chronic pain and other symptoms as well."

—Eric Robins, M.D. - Expert in treating chronic pain

This quote from the introduction to our friend, Nick Ortner's, book *The Tapping Solution For Pain Relief* inspires us to try this crazy tapping thing on everything, including chronic or even long standing pain.

Let's face it, pain causes stress, stress causes tension, fatigue and plenty of emotional responses that wear us down and make our lives miserable.

I suffer with chronic pain to varying degrees and nothing has been more effective than EFT tapping for relieving my pain. And I have had the great joy of sharing this healing practice with many, many people who have also had amazing results and relief.

Today I am encouraging you to be willing to try tapping, even though it's weird, it may not work right away and you don't believe me - try it anyway.

Set Up Statements:

"Even though I have this pain and part of me might be holding on, for whatever reason, conscious or unconscious, I choose to accept myself and all my feelings."

"Even though I've had this pain for so long and it's wearing me out, I choose to open to the healing with love and acceptance."

Reminder Statements:

(while tapping around on the body points)

"All this pain, all this nasty pain, it's really wearing me out. I've tried everything and I still have this pain…all this exhausting pain…this deep pain. I'd really like to let this go."

Pause, take a few deep breaths, close your eyes and check in with your body - your thoughts, emotions and memories.

You may be surprised at what arises. Be open to including the details from the past, such as limiting beliefs and fears or memories. Be as specific as possible and tell the truth.

"All this pain…this pain from the surgery…it just won't go away. I've had this for so long, nothing seems to work. All this pain…all this frustration…will this ever go away? I choose to listen to my body. What if I could relax a little bit? Letting go of the pain. I choose to open to the healing."

Remember to keep tapping until you feel relief. Then do another round with alternating statements of release, letting go, opening to healing and gratitude.

Healing Story:

"Chronic back problems from lifting my one year old son brought me to Meditation/Tapping class. I was working around the pain and now I'm finding that the tapping really helps. When I'm in pain I get anxious as well. What I love about tapping is that I can do it for myself anywhere and it helps me get to sleep more easily. Now I love to remember to use the practice and have more time without pain. I love the happy tapping." **Leslie**

Relieving Physical Pain

Set Up Statement:

While tapping on the side of both hands.

"Even though I have all this pain in my body, and part of me is holding on, I love and accept and forgive myself and I am safe."

After a round or two of tapping while focusing on the pain, you may begin a Releasing Round when the intensity begins to come down. Alter your Set Up Statement slightly and alternate what you say on each point:

"This remaining pain…I'd really like to let this go. This remaining pain…it's time to relax and let go. This remaining pain…it's safe to release and let go. This remaining pain…I'm beginning to be willing to let this go. This remaining pain…I'm open to the healing. This remaining pain…I'm listening to my body. This remaining pain… what if I could let go of the pain?"

Reminder Statements:

While tapping around on the body points.

"All this pain…all this pain in my body…all this pain…part of me is holding on. All this pain…I'd really like to let this go. Doesn't feel safe to relax. All this pain…it's been this way for so long. All this pain…"

Pause and check in with your body. Notice the intensity of the pain - where you feel it in your body - take a few slow, deep breaths. Also notice your thoughts and the story you are telling. When the intensity begins to come down, revise your Set Up Statement and tap for another round.

Set Up Statement:

"Even though I feel a bit more calm and relaxed, part of me is still holding on, for whatever reason, conscious or unconscious. And I choose to love and accept myself, just as I am."

Reminder Statements:

"Feeling a bit calmer…still feeling the pain…holding onto the pain…what if I can begin to relax and let go? This remaining pain…I'm listening to my body, relaxing and letting go, opening to the healing, releasing the pain now, allowing myself to relax. It's safe to let go."

Continue to tap until you feel relief from the intense feelings. Take a few deep breaths when you next feel the pain and tap. Continue this practice each day as you continue to release and heal.

Complete your practice with Happy Tapping:

"I'm so grateful for the healing…feeling more comfortable. I am safe, grateful for the healing…my body is my teacher. I'm feeling so much calmer now, making healthy choices. I'm giving my body love

and support. I'm grateful for my strong, flexible, healthy body. Thank you, thank you, thank you!"

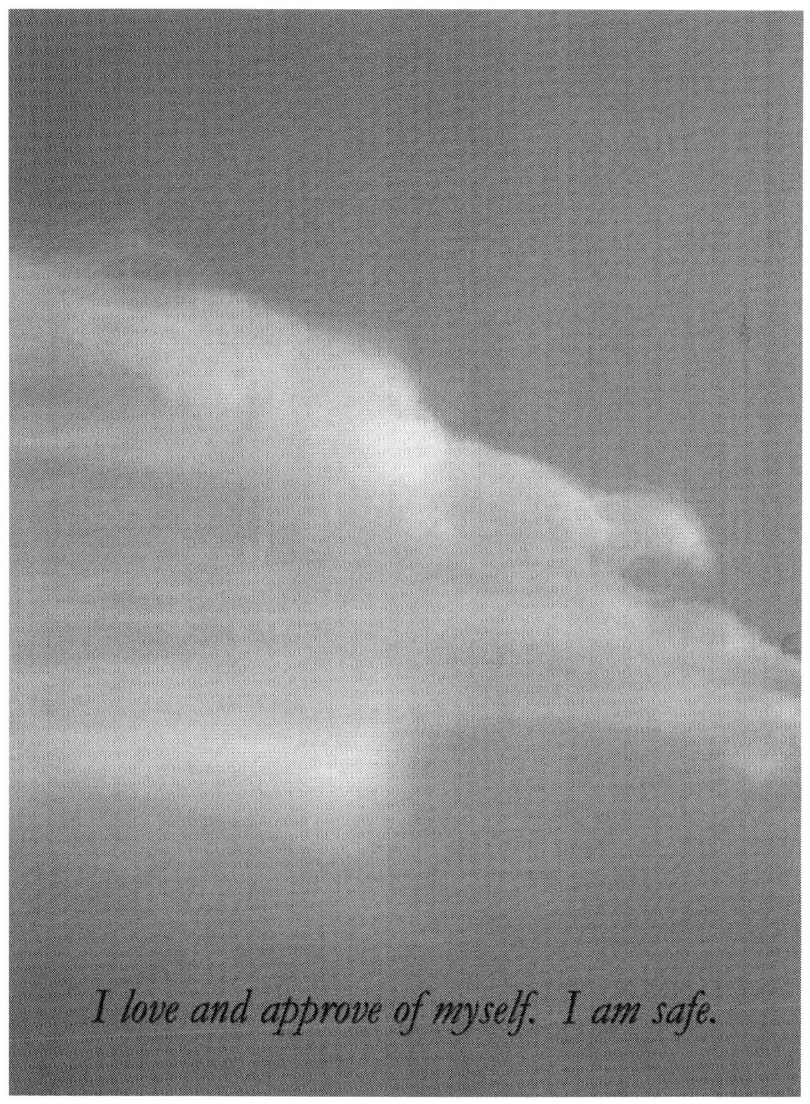

Is My Pain Physical or Emotional or Both?

As you continue down the path of practicing Meditation and Emotional Freedom Technique (EFT) tapping to support your health and well-being, you may have already enjoyed the amazing benefits of pain relief with this practice.

Pain relief is one of the simplest and most effective applications for EFT.

Thank goodness for EFT! It's simply magic.

If you have yet to try tapping or have yet to truly integrate it into your self-care, now is the time to begin.

When I first learned tapping, it was for relief of really nasty chronic back pain. I tapped every day for two weeks and the pain was gone! Really. It's never come back except briefly when

I changed my exercise routine. Yes, it scared me and I tapped and went right back to the strength training exercises that had been working for me. Within three days, the pain was gone. Yay!

And practice a little bit every day to really see results.

You also may have discovered that pain is not simply physical. Often we have strong emotions, memories and beliefs associated with the pain. This is significant.

It can be effective to ask for clarity in your Meditation and then tap on the information that is revealed about the sadness, anger, fear or frustration that arises with the physical pain.

Simply say, "*All this sadness,*" or "*All this fear,*" as you tap around on the body points.

Then check in with your physical symptoms and sensations. Most often you will gain relief, clarity and ease with the physical pain.

Remember to add Choice Statements to your final round as you relax and let go of the pain:

"I now choose to relax and let go."
"I choose to accept this healing now."
"I give thanks for the comfort and ease that I feel."

May this practice help you to be a healthier and a happier you.

Healing Story:

"I wanted to thank you for sharing the EFT process with me. I have been using it every day with great results. During our training I was experiencing pain in my left shoulder, due to some heavy duty yard work I had done a few days earlier. I used the tapping training and the pain was gone that evening. When I experienced a little discomfort over the next few days, I repeated the EFT and it was fantastic, the pain was gone. It is now four days since you gave us the training, I have no more pain or discomfort in my left shoulder.

I did not take any aspirin during this time, which is what I would usually do. Thank You!, Thank You!, Thank You!

I know I will use the EFT for the rest of my life to release any pain I may have. From your training, I know that EFT may be used to release any negative emotions that I may encounter, and we all have them at one time or another, allowing me the ability to correct imbalances and blockages, so they will not physically impact me. Again, Thank You!" **Joyce Kephalos**

Wisdom of Your Body

One way to find relief, that helps us move beyond taking a pill or searching the internet, is to get in touch with your Body Wisdom. You may call this intuition, guidance, knowing or even magic.

I have found that when I have a question about what is happening in my body - my head wants to figure out a solution and Do something. When I take the time to slow down, get quiet and ask my body for information, I usually get a different answer and somehow wiser information.

I might ask "What is it I need to know or understand?"

Then I listen with my heart for the answer.

This may take some time and patience. I feel that I am tuning in to my Body Wisdom and Intuition - a part of my consciousness that is not confined to intellect or intelligence.

My body might say, "Slow Down." or "Time to Rest."

It is most often a Being response, rather than a Doing.

Asking For Guidance From a Body Part or Symptom

Another way to gain clarity about your self-care may be to practice communicating with your body, as if it has a voice.

When you have tension, pain or discomfort in your back, for instance, you might settle yourself down and bring your awareness to your back. Gently pat your heart and say, **"There, there, I'm listening. How can I help you?"**

Then wait patiently for an answer from your body. You may receive words, phrases, thoughts, or memories. At times my body will show me a behavior or treatment that will be helpful.

You are tuning into your unique Body Wisdom and Guidance. I also find that trusting and acting on the guidance helps to encourage the connection and effectiveness.

This practice works just as well for emotional issues. When I feel anxious and ask my Body Wisdom for guidance, my body will say "Go outside." This helps me to calm down, especially when I've been inside for a while.

Healing Story:

"It was my good fortune to meet Becca. Clearly, I was a stress mess. My family and friends had gently suggested I was in need of some new stress management tools. Was it the skin rash that I had for a year, my inability to complete a sentence due to brain fog; bruxism, hair loss, exhaustion, insomnia, loss of executive functions; forgetfulness, withdrawal from life, whining, and/or too much wine that alerted them? My stress management tools were inadequate. At age 67, I needed a refresher course in stress management and Becca turned out to be the perfect coach for me.

In my first meeting, Becca quickly assessed my situation. In the following months, Becca introduced me to EFT and other complementary stress-reducing techniques including: listening to your body, visioning, meditation, deep breathing, and mindfulness. Also, she taught me how to make very mighty sighs which are quite useful when alone or in the presence of others. I am now healing and have diminished my stress level according to my cortisol tests, clear skin, full head of healthy hair, sweet dreams during a full-night's sleep, and other important measures, i.e. my daughter actually wants to come home for a visit and bring her two-year old. And, my husband says he will now have dinner with me without hesitation as I have recovered my sense of humor, laugh out loud, and no longer go from hello to indignation in 45 seconds or less.

Before I met Becca, the hobgoblins of stress were wreaking havoc on my mind, body, spirit, and relationships. My immune system was overtaxed and failing to do its job. All the lotions, potions, and pills I was taking did not bring relief from my symptoms and frequently had unwelcome side effects. Stress is a mystery. Why does it choose one person over another? What causes it to overwhelm individuals without warning? I cannot say that I have learned much about the complexities of stress. However, I have learned effective techniques to battle it. I am very pleased that Becca has written this book to share them with everyone." **BF**

PART 3

Emotional Healing

Anger – Powerful Energy for Healing

We all have experienced anger at one time or another. Growing up in my family, it was my father who was always angry, my mother who was always sad and my younger brother and I were expected to do as we were told and remain invisible. Not a particularly healthy environment.

For most of my young adult life I made every effort to be a good girl, to not cause any upset for anyone and to keep a low profile. Until one day my landlord came into my house without my permission. Whew! I was on the phone with him with a calm, clear and clearly angry message about what he had done. I learned to express myself clearly, to respond to the energy of anger appropriately, and to ask for what I needed.

Now I seldom feel anger unless I witness an injustice and am inspired to take action to make a difference to the best of my ability. I always want to be part of the solution, rather than part of the problem.

If you have a pattern of feeling anger often, you are most likely carrying resentment, frustration or unresolved sadness and grief from the past. Tapping is very effective in relieving the intensity of anger to clear and resolve past hurts and to bring clarity about how to respond appropriately.

You may bring to mind a specific event or person while you tap around on the body points until you feel relief. Or one of the Bundling techniques will work well to acknowledge and release a pattern that you are noticing in your life and in your relationships.

Set Up Statement:

"Even though I feel so angry I could scream, I'd really like to let this go. Whatever part of me is holding on, for whatever reason, conscious or unconscious, I now choose to relax and let go with love and acceptance for myself and everyone else involved."

Reminder Statements:

while tapping around on the body points:

"Feeling so angry...all this anger...I'm really feeling it in my body. I'd really like to let this go. Feeling so much anger and I'm holding it in my body. So much anger...I feel like I could scream. Letting the energy move. So much anger...This isn't OK with me. It's OK to feel these feelings and open to the healing."

Keep tapping until you feel the intensity coming down. Breathe deeply. Perhaps tell the story about what happened while you tap around on the body points or on your favorite tapping points using your own words.

When you begin to feel more calm and perhaps have greater insight about the situation, pause and check in with your body, thoughts and emotions and then tap again using release statements:

"Feeling a bit calmer, still not ready to let go of this anger. Allowing my body to relax just a little bit... Allowing the energy to move... I'm willing to begin to consider letting this go. Part of me knows how to forgive and let go. Opening to a new way of being...Giving myself permission to relax and let go of

the past…I can respond more wisely now. Relaxing and letting go…"

Give thanks for the healing, for the clarity, for your capacity for forgiveness and ability to communicate with calm and compassion.

Anxiety & Stress

More and more we are learning that anxiety stems from constantly focusing on the past or the future. When we practice keeping our awareness in the present moment, we are more able to relieve anxiety and stress. One of the biggest benefits of EFT tapping practice is the ability to acknowledge and release the past and calm our body and mind in the present moment, so that we can make healthy choices about our self-care and our response to current challenges.

Set Up Statements:

"Even though I feel anxious most of the time and part of me is holding onto this old pattern, for whatever reason, conscious or unconscious. I choose to honor all of my feelings with love and acceptance."

"Even though I feel so much stress, and I can't seem to slow down, no matter what I do. I acknowledge how I feel and where I am right now."

Reminder Statements:

(Remember to use your own words and even tell the story as you tap around on the body points, speaking out loud or silently.)

"I feel so anxious and stressed. So much anxiety...I can feel it in my body. Can't slow down... can't quiet my mind...I feel guilty when I rest. Where is this coming from? All this anxiety and stress...always pushing myself...all this anxiety... This is really wearing me out!"

Rest for a few moments, with your eyes closed and check in with your body. Notice the emotions, thoughts and memories that arise.

You may go back to the Set Up Statement with more information:

"Even though I feel a little bit more relaxed, part of me is still holding on because I feel more anxious when I relax. So I'm acknowledging this with love and acceptance."

Another round of tapping on the body points until you feel relief:

"Feeling a little bit more relaxed...Can't slow down... there's the anxiety again... Where does this come from? Is this current or from the past? All this anxiety that I'm holding in my body... What if I could relax just a little bit, and give myself a break. Telling the story...beginning to be willing to slow down, be gentle with myself... releasing the anxiety and stress... letting go... allowing myself to feel the feelings and let the energy move..."

See if you can take a little time following your meditation and tapping practice to write down what you have learned about this pattern in your life. The anxiety you feel may be valid for your current circumstances. You can take action to resolve whatever is concerning you.

If this has been a long term issue for you, you may ask for guidance about a time in your past where you decided that you were not safe, that you couldn't have what you needed. There may be very convincing limiting beliefs and fears that are still holding you back.

The good news is that you can acknowledge and release those old limiting beliefs and fears that are no longer serving you.

Healing Story:

"I want to let you know of my positive experience with the Meditation and EFT that I learned in your weekly class. I was experiencing severe back and leg pain earlier this year. The pain got so severe that I needed to use crutches in order to walk. I had trouble finding a comfortable position to sleep so consequently my sleep was very fretful and interrupted. I was diagnosed with spinal stenosis and was prescribed pain medication. I would not take narcotic pain medication but started taking NSAIDs, which really upset my digestive system. I again consulted my physician and it was recommended that I have spinal surgery. I decided against the surgery and started attending the meditation and EFT classes.

I practiced the methods I learned in class at home as well. Gradually, my pain lessened and finally and miraculously disappeared! It is incredible how different I now feel and I am pain free, thanks to these methods and you! I can't thank you enough for introducing me to this incredible method." **Rosemarie Vertulo**

Bundling Baggage to Heal the Past

One of the first tapping techniques I learned was called the **Personal Peace Process**. It involved making a list of all of the events, relationships and circumstances from the past that you want to heal, then tapping on one item each day until you have reduced the intensity of everything on the list.

Then I learned a much quicker and more effective way to heal and release the past called **Bundling Baggage**.

1. **Choose the topic** for your tapping session - an illness, a relationship, an event, such as an accident or a big disappointment. You might even choose your childhood or past relationship for the session.
2. Imagine that all of the details of your chosen topic are placed in front of you in a big pile.
3. **Describe** the pile visually - size, color, shape, smell - is it like a big pile of steaming dung?

Is it as big as a car, as big as a house, as big as a mountain?

4. Take note of the **intensity of the pile** when you begin. On a scale of 0 to 10, with 10 being the highest, how intense does the pile seem?

5. Tap on the pile with your **Set Up Statement**:

"*Even though I have this big, steamy pile - and part of me is holding on - for whatever reason, I choose to release and let go with love and acceptance.*"

"*Even though I have this huge pile - it's as big as my house and it's dark and scary looking, part of me is holding on, for whatever reason - maybe it's keeping me safe. I now choose to be open and release this pile. I love, accept and forgive myself, and I am safe.*"

6. **Reminder Statements** (tapping around on the body points):

"*This big, steamy pile…big steamy pile…big steamy pile... It really stinks! This big, steamy pile in front of me…*"

Has it changed? Gotten smaller? Transformed into something else?

7. Continue with a revised Set Up Statement and tap around some more on the body points.

8. You may be amazed that the pile gets smaller, less intense and may even transform into something else.

When I first did this tapping exercise I started with a swamp and it turned into a meadow. I was amazed!

Be gentle with yourself - be playful with this process –pretend you can see the pile.

Your subconscious mind works with imagery and may surprise you with information and details you haven't expected. Allow this to be light and enjoyable.

Your willingness to release the past is the key to releasing your accumulated baggage and the effect it has had on your life and health.

Using Imagery with Tapping to Heal & Release the Past

Our subconscious minds respond to images. When we visualize all of our baggage in a big stinky pile, we can tap on the past without stirring up the details of what happened. This is a powerful and playful way to heal and release the past. You may choose a particular memory or circumstance of imaging sweeping everything from the past out of your body and into the pile.

Link to Stinky Pile #1 video:
https://www.youtube.com/watch?v=2R_GXjEaBgA

Link to Stinky Pile #2 video:
https://www.youtube.com/watch?v=jUlqVql_n3I

Childhood Trauma – Connecting with Your Younger Self

EFT tapping is the most effective healing modality for healing childhood trauma. When I was twelve years old my mother had a nervous breakdown. She was diagnosed as manic depressive, was mostly depressed and stayed in bed after that. This condition is now called biopolar disorder and much has improved in the treatment and relief of the condition.

In my family this event meant that I became the main caregiver in the family and my childhood was effectively over. I took it upon myself to get good grades, clean the house, cook and take care of my younger brother and my mother. Along with all of that I did my best to stay clear of my father's alcoholic rages and verbal abuse.

After I left home at 18 I got married, because I didn't know what else to do, I worked as a secretary and became a very high functioning workaholic. I coped by staying busy and did not remember my childhood. I discovered twelve step recovery groups and therapy when my mother died when I was 33. I was fortunate to begin to heal and recover.

Most everyone I've ever worked with has had traumatic experiences such as alcoholism, mental illness, death of loved ones or financial losses and accidents in their past. We may or may not be aware of how these traumas continue to affect us in the present. This is where tapping and meditation can be extremely helpful in healing the past, uncovering unconscious limiting beliefs and fears and allowing us to life more fully in the present with strength, balance, harmony and peace.

Please refer to the section on Matrix Reimprinting in this book and seek out a certified EFT and Matrix practitioner to support you with your healing. Therapists who specialize in healing childhood trauma are also available to support you.

Emotional Impacts of Chronic Pain

If you have been on this earth for any length of time, you have undoubtedly experienced physical pain from an injury, accident, illness or other calamity. When we were children our parent's response to our cries of pain may have ranged from a hug and a bandaid to a rush to the emergency room. Aspirin was usually the treatment for any headache or minor pain in my family. Antiseptic was applied to scrapes and cuts and most everything was healed and relieved in a day or two.

As an adult I have developed arthritis and degenerative disc disease, resulting in chronic pain that is both frustrating and exhausting. My personal approach to dealing with chronic pain has been to seek physical therapy, acupuncture, massage and, when all else fails, rest and patience. Honestly, my last resort is to seek medication or medical treatment by a physician.

As you may have gathered, I find that one of the most effective ways to deal with chronic pain and the accompanying frustration, exhaustion, anger, fear and depression is dedicated daily self-care, relaxation techniques, meditation and tapping to reduce the intensity of the emotions. Allow the energy to move through the body, to relieve symptoms and to promote the natural healing process.

When you have done all that you can to relieve chronic pain, including medication and/or medical assistance, remember that meditation and tapping is extremely effective for relieving stress and gaining greater clarity about your situation.

Forgiveness & Letting Go of the Past

Bring to mind a person or circumstance that you would like to forgive. Make sure to include yourself in your forgiveness practice. What has happened that you regret or can't stop blaming yourself for? Something that you did or failed to do that you are still holding on to. Notice the intensity of the feelings of regret, resentment, sadness and loss.

Set Up Statements

(while tapping on the side of both hands):

"Even though I can't forgive this person, part of me is holding on to this hurt, for whatever reason, I choose to deeply and completely accept myself and all my feelings."

"Even though I have this painful memory, part of me is not ready to let this go. And a wiser, bigger part of me is ready to heal and forgive. I want that wiser part of me to win. And I deeply and completely love and accept myself, just as I am."

"I love and accept and forgive myself and everyone else involved."

Reminder Statements

(tapping around on the 10 body points): *"This hurtful event... Worst time of my life... I can't let this go. This painful memory...I trusted this person. And they lied to me. This really hurt. Part of me is still holding on to this. This painful event... All the hurt and heartbreak... I'd really like to forgive and let this go...*

When you begin to feel relief from your painful memory, tap a few more rounds with Choice Statements as you begin to forgive and let go:

I want to let this go... I can't let this go. This is really holding me back in my relationships."

"This painful memory...I'd really like to let it go. This painful memory...It's time to forgive and let this go. The part of me that is holding on, maybe it's keeping me safe. I'm willing to relax and let go of this memory now. Any part of me that's holding on, I choose to forgive myself and everyone else involved. I'm open to the healing. It's safe to let go of the past. I'm open to begin to trust in my relationships."

Remember to use your own words, tell the story while you tap. Be gentle with yourself and take some time to rest, journal and open to a new way of being.

Healing Relationships – Family & Friends

Unless you are living in a hut in the woods, with no contact with other humans, you undoubtedly have times when you have challenges with relationships. Those closest to us are most likely to push our buttons more than people we interact with less often. Our parents, siblings, children and spouses seem to be experts at causing conflict and disagreements.

We may be more or less aware that we are reenacting family dynamics learned in childhood. It has been my experience that conflict in the present is most often connected to unresolved issues from the past.

You may notice a pattern in your relationships with friends. Some you feel more comfortable with and some not so much. I believe that we are always given opportunities to learn, grow and become clearer about what feels good to us and what does not feel good. We always have a choice about how we respond and interact. I continue to be guided by the Golden Rule as taught to me by my grandmother – do unto others as you would have them do unto you. Or treat others as you would like to be treated.

When you are in the throes of a difficult relationship you may find resolution by focusing on the person involved while acknowledging the emotions you are feeling while **tapping around on the body points** until you feel calmer, clearer and more open to either a clearing conversation or a completing conversation. You may find it helpful to write a letter to outline your experience, which may or may not be sent, as you choose. This process can work wonders even with people who have died or are no longer close to us. We are always capable of learning and growing in our relationships, thank goodness!

Limiting Beliefs & Fears

In my training as an EFT Master we learned about the benefits of working with the various parts of our selves. There is a powerful part of each of us that holds us back and reminds us of our Limiting Beliefs and Fears.

You may call this aspect of self your ego, personality, younger self or simply your inner critic. And the truth is that we all also have an aspect of self that is clear, confident, wise and bold!

This is why we say in our Set Up statements - *"whatever part of me is holding me back, consciously or unconsciously, for whatever reason, I'm acknowledging these feelings."*

You might also communicate with this doubting and fearful part of yourself in your meditation or in your journal. Here's an example:

Me: (speaking to the doubting part) *Why are you holding me back?*
Doubter: *My job is to protect you.*
Me: *How are you protecting me?*
Doubter: *By keeping you safe from getting hurt.*

Me: *Thank you for protecting me. I'd really like to give you a new job.*
Doubter: *But I've been protecting you your whole life.*
Me: *I appreciate that, and now I'd like to have your help with making healthy choices and moving forward with ease.*
Doubter: *I'm not sure how to do that. Hurtful things have happened.*
Me: *I have survived all of the things that have happened and they have taught me many important lessons.*
Doubter: *Maybe I could try.*
Me: *OK. Thank you so much. You are doing a great job. So let's practice releasing the old Limiting Beliefs and Fears.*

See what I mean? I know you all have your critical voice - your version of how this part of your self holds you back. I encourage you to use your daily practice of Meditation and Tapping to acknowledge the doubt and fear. There is great benefit in bringing these aspects to light.

I'd love to hear from you about how these practices are helping you step into your strong, confident and brilliant self!

Relieving Grief & Sadness

We all experience loss as a part of life. Most of us associate grief and sadness with the loss of life, love, health or security. However, grief can be triggered by any major change, such as moving to a new home, leaving for college, getting married or even a promotion at work. All of these seeming positive experiences include change in some form and can trigger grief and sadness.

With EFT we are not attempting to eliminate the grief and sadness. We are addressing the issues with the intention of relieving the intensity and the heaviness associated with change and loss. Many of the symptoms of grief and sadness, such as fatigue, confusion, anxiety, fear and stress can be relieved quite effectively with a few rounds of tapping. Journaling may also be very helpful with processing loss.

Tapping To Relieve Grief & Sadness

Set Up Statements:

"Even though I'm feeling so sad and part of me is holding on to this grief, for whatever reason, conscious or unconscious, I honor all of my feelings with love and acceptance."

"Even though this grief is weighing me down, I choose to acknowledge my feelings and accept myself just as I am."

"Even though this sadness feels endless and uncomfortable, part of me is holding onto the past, for whatever reason, conscious or unconscious, I choose to relax and let go, just a little bit. I'm open to the healing and I love, accept and forgive myself and everyone else involved."

Reminder Statements:

"Feeling so sad...all this sadness...all this grief...It feels so heavy and uncomfortable. All this sadness... grieving the loss... deep sadness... Can't seem to move past this. This deep sadness, feeling it in my body... weighing me down... all this sadness... Will I ever feel better?"

Take a deep breath and check in with your body, your thoughts and emotions. Has the intensity changed, increased or decreased? Have you gained clarity about your situation? Have there been changes in your energy level, your breathing, your physical sensations? Often when we are tapping we notice the tension and awareness move in the body. I take this as a good sign, that we are moving the energy and allowing the feelings to move as well.

When you begin to feel relief, begin to add Releasing Statements to your tapping rounds:

"Even though I feel a little bit calmer and clearer, part of me might still be holding on. I now choose to relax and allow the energy to move. I'm open to the healing with love and acceptance."

Reminder Statements –alternating on the points:

"This remaining sadness… I'm willing to begin to let it go. This remaining sadness… It's OK to feel these feelings. This remaining grief and sadness… being gentle with myself…so much sadness…What if I could allow the feelings? I'm relaxing and letting go, taking as long as it takes, allowing the energy to move, releasing the tension and pain."

Stress Relief – Calming Down the Primitive Brain

While tapping on the Karate Chop points on the side of both hands:

"Even though I'm feeling stressed, part of me might be holding on, for whatever reason, conscious or unconscious. I choose to relax and let go of the stress with love and acceptance."

"Even though it's all just too much right now, I choose to relax and let go of the stress. I love and accept myself and all of my feelings."

Reminder Statements - tapping on the 10 body points:

***Eyebrow points with both hands*:** All this stress.
***Outside eyes*:** All this stress that I'm holding in my body.
***Under eyes*:** All this stress about my schedule.
***Under nose*:** All this stress. It's just too much!
***Under mouth*:** These feelings are really wearing me out.
***Collar bones*:** All this stress.
***Under arms*:** I'd really like to let it go.
***Ribs*:** All this stress is wearing me out and I'm afraid I won't be able to work.
Inside wrists: I'm not sleeping well and I'm tired all of the time.
Top of head: I acknowledge this stress and allow the energy to move.

Continue to tap until you feel relief from the stressful feelings.

When you begin to feel some relief, you may begin to use Choice Statements, such as: *"I now choose to release this remaining stress and pressure. I choose to relax and slow down. I release this stress from my tissues, my fluids, my muscles, my bones and my organs. I choose to give myself permission to relax in body, mind and spirit. I am open to patience and acceptance for myself and others."*

Complete your tapping practice with a **Positive Round**, tapping while you say all that you are grateful for and all that you wish to experience. **Happy tapping!**

PART 4

Try It On Everything

I've seen results tapping with so many clients that I thought I'd share the variety of possibilities with you: anxiety, fatigue, stress, insomnia, anger, resentment, recovering from a fall or an accident, confusion, physical pain, fear, feeling stuck, and so much more. Of course, not everything is completely cleared in one or even a few tapping sessions.

It is important to be specific, be willing to tell the truth, to see the patterns, habits and beliefs that accompany the issue and to be willing to dig a bit into the underlying causes.

This Takes Courage

It's not easy to look within and be honest about what's true. We would much rather avoid the issue, distract ourselves, take a pill or put off getting real about what is holding us back in life.

Sometimes the cause is external circumstances, other people, the powers that be. When that is true, we still have a choice about how we respond.

Most often our difficulties are self-inflicted. We've always pushed ourselves, worked too hard, not rested enough, eaten well or given ourselves a break.

It's Time To Ease Up On Yourself

Remember that the definition of insanity is to continue to do the same things while expecting different results!!

I was inspired to pick up Nick Ortner's book, *The Tapping Solution For Pain Relief* and guess what?

On Page 153 to 160 Nick talks about creating Healthy Boundaries.

He suggests that we ask ourselves, "Is it safe to let go of this pain?"

Affirmations & Tapping

"I love and approve of myself and I trust the process of life.

I am safe."

–Affirmation to relieve anxiety by Louise L. Hay in *You Can Heal Your Life*

I've been reading and appreciating Louise Hay's book for over thirty years. Her approach to healing through affirmations and insights about the emotional connections to our physical conditions has inspired me deeply.

Now I add tapping to my affirmation practice and so does Louise!

Before her passing she was interviewed by Nick Ortner with The Tapping Solution and he honored her as a beloved teacher on the spiritual path. My copy of this book falls open to the affirmations for relieving pain, anxiety and stress. Nothing has relieved my life-long anxiety as effectively as EFT.

I must admit, that it did take some time. We know that EFT tapping is amazingly effective to relieve acute pain, such as headaches, in the moment. It's also effective for healing and releasing the past, which does take some time...

For most of my life, until recently, I pushed myself and always felt like something was wrong. I believe these feelings stemmed from childhood trauma. As I have uncovered my memories from childhood, I have been able to grieve the losses, forgive myself and others and have been able to enjoy greater ease in my current life.

These have been profound healings for me and I want to share that with all of you.

Accessing & Trusting Your Body Wisdom

When we are experiencing stress and feel fear, anxiety, sadness or other strong emotions, our system goes into fight, flight or freeze mode. Stress hormones flow through the nervous system and we shift into survival mode. This natural response shuts down the frontal lobes of the brain and causes brain fog. We are less able to make healthy choices about how to respond to our circumstances.

As long as you are not actually in an unsafe environment, the best response is to slow down, take some deep breaths and bring your awareness down into your body. Feel your connection to the earth. Drink some water. Pat your heart. If you are able to move physically away from others, even for a few moments, give yourself permission to close your eyes, tap around on the body points and ask for guidance from your body wisdom.

Including your whole body in your meditation practice is extremely helpful in accessing body wisdom and guidance. We often keep our awareness in our heads while there is tremendous wisdom and neurological cells in all parts of our bodies, especially in the gut. Gut instinct really is a good thing. In meditation, I often ask, "what is it I need to know and understand?" Then I listen with my heart (rather than my head) for the answer.

Abundance & Financial Issues

For such a universal issue as financial fears and anxiety, EFT is one of the most effective techniques I have found for healing limiting beliefs and fears and opening to greater ease and abundance. Perhaps you were raised, as I was, with a great deal of conversation about insufficient income, fights at the dinner table about money and those so familiar stories like "money doesn't grow on trees," "we work hard to put food on the table and keep a roof over our heads," and "there is never enough to go around." Our family beliefs stay with us until we consciously release them.

All the years I worked in the corporate world and then as a successful entrepreneur I was always anxious about money and feeling that there wasn't enough. This led to workaholism, chronic anxiety and pushing myself to exhaustion. For years I studied and practiced affirmations and abundance practices and still felt that something was wrong with me.

When I learned and began to practice EFT, I was finally able to uncover my limiting beliefs and fears from the past and begin to ease up on myself. Listening to my internal dialog about money was extremely helpful in bringing to light all of the ways I had internalized my parents and grandmothers beliefs and experiences.

My beloved teacher, Louise Hay would say: "Just having money is not enough. We want to enjoy the money." Allow yourself to have pleasure with money. Have fun with money. What old belief is stopping you?

"When the stress response calms and we come out of survival/fight or flight mode, we have more access to our own natural brilliance!"

–Margaret M. Lynch in "The 7 Levels of Wealth Manifestation"

Here's where you might begin:

Set up Statement: *"Even though I have so much fear and anxiety around money and this is really holding me back in life, I'm acknowledging my feelings. Whatever part of me that's holding on, for whatever reason, conscious or unconscious, I now choose to relax and release the past. I release the fear and open to the healing with love and acceptance. I love and accept and forgive myself and everyone who taught me to worry and fret."*

Reminder Statements: *"All this fear…all this worry…It's really holding me back. I don't feel safe. No matter how hard I work, I always feel behind. Anxious about money…There's never enough…Acknowledging my feelings…I wonder where this comes from? Allowing the energy to move…Open to clarity and calm… Releasing the past."*

Checking In: Close your eyes and take a few moments to check in with your thoughts, emotions and the sensations in your body. Has the intensity of the fear come down, stayed the same, or increased? Notice the story you're telling yourself. Continue tapping on the feelings and tell the story as you tap until you begin to feel relief, then begin a Releasing round – alternating what you say on the points.

Releasing Round:

"*This remaining fear…I'd really like to let it go. This remaining anxiety about money...It's time to relax and let it go. This old fear and anxiety… I'm ready to open up to a new way of being. This old story…I honor all my feelings. I'm relaxing and letting go. Feeling so much better… Relaxing and letting go…I'm open to the healing in my body, mind and spirit.*"

Give thanks for the guidance, the healing and the willingness to move forward with clarity, confidence and courage.

EFT Movie Technique

We all have our stories. I know I do. Just the other day I told an old friend about being diagnosed with degenerative disc disease a few years ago. She graciously invited me to tell the story differently, to continue to allow my body to heal and be strong.

Then I was able to tell her how strong and healthy I've been with my self-care, strength training, EFT and acupuncture. Yay!

There is a powerful EFT technique, called the ***Movie Technique***, developed by Gary Craig, the founder of EFT. It allows us to see the events of our lives as if they are appearing on a movie screen - while tapping to relieve the stress and intensity of the event.

1. Choose a specific event that you would like to heal and relieve.
2. In your imagination, create a short movie - perhaps 2 or 3 minutes - of this event.

3. Concentrate on the emotions and physical feelings from this event. ***What are you seeing, hearing, smelling and tasting?***
4. Imaging that you are sitting in the back of the theater to view this movie - perhaps it's in black and white if the emotions are intense.
5. Choose a title for the movie, such as *"This diagnosis movie"* or *"This accident movie."*
6. Play the movie in your head and notice the intensity you are feeling *now*, as you imagine it, on a scale of 0 to 10, with 10 being the most intense.
7. Do several rounds of tapping on the body points on *"This _______ movie."* You can say the words out loud or silently, if you prefer.
8. Check in with the intensity of the movie. Stop when you feel the intensity rising and continue to tap, as you gently move through the movie.
9. Play the movie again and tap around the points again, several times, if necessary, until you feel relief - stopping when you feel the intensity. We are acknowledging the feelings and releasing the stress as we tap and calming the stress in response to this memory.
10. Continue until you can run through the entire movie with the intensity down to a 0. See if you can narrate the movie and not feel the intensity.

May this practice help you to heal and release the past with love and acceptance.

Happy Tapping – Gratitude Tapping

Be Thankful

Be thankful that you don't already have everything you desire. If you did, what would there be to look forward to?
Be thankful when you don't know something. It gives you the opportunity to learn.
Be thankful for the difficult times. During those times you grow.
Be thankful for your limitations, because they give you opportunities for improvement.
Be thankful for each new challenge, because it will build your strength and character.
Be thankful for your mistakes. They will teach you valuable lessons.
Be thankful when you're tired and weary, because it means you've made a difference.
It is easy to be thankful for the good things. A life of rich fulfillment comes to those who are also thankful for the setbacks.

GRATITUDE can turn a negative into a positive.

Find a way to be thankful for your troubles

and they can become your blessings.

–Author Unknown

Express your gratitude while tapping around on the body points:

- **Eyebrows:** *"I am so grateful for my health."*
- **Side of Eyes:** *"I'm grateful to be strong, flexible and energetic."*
- **Under Eyes:** *"I'm so glad I have clear eyesight, sound hearing and the ability to smell and taste my food."*
- **Under Nose**: *"I'm grateful for my home."*
- **Chin:** *"Thank you for all of the love and connection in my family and friends."*
- **Collarbones:** *"I give thanks for my ability to think and make healthy choices about my self-care."*
- **Under Arms:** *"I'm grateful for my bed and a good night's sleep."*
- **Ribs:** *"Thank you for the rain; thank you for the sunshine."*
- **Wrists:** *"I appreciate the opportunity to be of service to others in my work and in my community."*
- **Top of Head:** *"I am so happy and grateful for my pets!"*

Give yourself permission to stop for a few minutes, find a quiet place to settle down and connect with all of the blessings in your life.

Happy Tapping!

Healthy Relationships & Communication

A great deal of our stress, confusion and difficulties in life revolve around our relationships, especially close relationships with family, spouses, children and close friends. Tapping is a wonderful practice to gain clarity, guidance and to relieve the painful dynamics we experience in relationships.

One simple way to utilize tapping to improve relationships is to simply sit quietly and think about the person that is pushing your buttons. Tap while you feel the feelings, tell the story and allow the energy to move.

One powerful question you might ask is: "what does this remind me of?" There is a very good chance that this person reminds you (consciously or unconsciously) of your mother, father, sister or brother. It might not even be what they are saying, it may simply be their tone of voice that triggers you.

Set Up Statement:

"Even though ________ is really making me angry. I'm acknowledging my feelings and allowing the energy to move. Even though we are not communicating, I'm willing to release this anger and open to the healing. Whatever part of me that's holding on, consciously or unconsciously, I now choose to relax and accept myself and all of my feelings."

Reminder Statements:

"Feeling so angry! He/she is pushing my buttons. This isn't fair... I'm not being heard. Really feeling this in my body...I just want to scream! All this anger...It's holding me back. Doesn't feel good. All this anger and confusion...I'd really like to let this go. Feeling so uncomfortable...What if I can take a few deep breaths now? Relaxing and letting go."

Check in with your emotions, thoughts and physical sensations. What comes up for you? What does this situation remind you of? Is there a pattern here? Ask for guidance about how to come back to harmony and peace.

Releasing Round:

"This remaining anger... I'd really like to let this go. This remaining anger and confusion... It's time to let this go. This remaining fear and frustration...I'm acknowledging these feelings. Opening to patience and understanding...What if I can walk away and cool down? This remaining anger... Releasing and letting go. Releasing the anger from my bones, muscles, organs and fluids. Relaxing and letting go..."

You might take some time to write in your journal about what is unfolding between you and this person. Get it all out of your system. Writing down all of your grievances and tearing up the paper can be very satisfying. You may never deliver this to the other person unless you have been able to calm down and be clear and kind to request resolution.

Remember to give thanks and be open to the energy shift between you and your friends and loved ones. The more you are able to release the past, be clear and patient with other, the better your relationships will be and the less stress you will experience.

Procrastination – What Are You Avoiding?

If you, like me, live with chronic pain, you might want to ask yourself - what am I avoiding?

- Is there someone you are avoiding seeing or speaking to?
- Are you putting off important health care appointments?
- Where in your life are you procrastinating?
- Are you pushing yourself and avoiding rest?
- What is the last thing you are willing to pay attention to?

OK, confession time. As I sit here at my desk, gazing out at the hummingbirds zipping in and out of my garden this morning, I am looking at the piles all around me on my desk and, once again, putting off (procrastinating!) doing my filing and organizing.

- I know that the stuff is taking up space in my consciousness.
- I know that it will only take a few minutes to clear it up.
- I know that I will feel so proud of myself when I do it!
- I know that putting it off is not serving me.
- And still I procrastinate!

What in your life are you avoiding?

Might your willingness to stop avoiding something - anything - in your life help heal your chronic pain?

Will you join me in making a commitment right now to choosing one thing you will pay attention to today that will relieve some of the pressure you put on yourself?

Let's do this!

Do not put it off for one more minute, one more hour, one more day!

Relaxation Techniques – Progressive Relaxation

I learned this technique as a Deep Relaxation practice to offer at the end of Gentle Yoga classes. This is also a wonderful practice to unwind, unplug and relax before going to sleep. You might record these instructions, so that you can listen while you relax. Once you are settled down and comfortable:

1. Breathe slowly and deeply as you allow your body to be supported. Relax into that support.
2. Beginning with the top of your head, imaging the breath relaxing your scalp.

3. Relax your forehead.
4. Relax the muscles around your eyes, allowing your eyes to relax.
5. Relax your jaw and throat.
6. Relax the muscles in your neck, rolling your head gently side to side.
7. Relax your shoulders, lifting your shoulders up to your ears and then relaxing them down.
8. Relax your arms and hands.
9. Relax all the muscles along your spine, down into your lower back.
10. Breathe down into your chest and abdomen, relaxing all of the muscles around your internal organs.

12. Open and soften the space around you heart, allowing loving kindness to flow throughout your body.

12. Relax your abdomen, pelvis and hips.
13. Feel the relaxation flowing down your legs to your knees, calves and ankles.
14. Relax your feet and your toes.
15. Take another deep and gentle breath and breathe out any remaining tension.
16. You may meditate for a few minutes, giving thanks for the day and allow yourself to drift into a deep and restful sleep. Do not be concerned if you fall asleep before getting all the way through your body.

Reprogramming Your Subconscious Mind

"By taking just a few extra seconds to stay with a positive experience – even the comfort in a single breath – you'll help turn a passing mental state into lasting neural structure."

–Rick Hanson Ph.D in "Hardwiring Happiness"

Rick Hanson is a psychologist and meditation teacher who shares simple and effective practices to tap the hidden power of everyday experiences to change your brain and your life for the better. The one I use most often is to observe a negative thought, pause and notice something that feels good, such as the warmth of the sun or a lovely cup of tea. Savor the good feeling for 10 seconds. Rinse and repeat.

This will gently and gradually rewire your neuro pathways from their innate tendency to notice potential danger to being able to stay calm, clear and joyful throughout your day. Yay!

Surrogate Tapping – Tapping For Others

When you have concerns for others, such as a child, a parent, a sibling, a friend or a pet, great healing is possible with Surrogate Tapping. I equate surrogate tapping to praying or well-wishing for others.

You always want to clear your own issues before tapping for others. For instance, if you are impatient with another person's behavior, it is best for you to tap on your own impatience. Surrogate tapping is not appropriate for changing the behavior of another person, as much as we would like to sometimes.

Begin your session by tapping on your own emotions, such as impatience, frustration, worry and concern. When you feel calm and clear, then you may begin to focus on the person to whom you would like to send love and healing.

I have learned two different approaches to Surrogate Tapping. One is to assume that you are the person and tap while tuning into their situation and experience. For example: *"I am (person's name) and I am tapping for relief from pain."* Then proceed through the Basic Recipe to acknowledge and release the pain.

Or you may tap as if you are speaking to them. For example, *"Even though you are feeling this pain, for whatever reason, conscious or unconscious, I know that you are wise, strong and capable of releasing this pain and opening to the healing with love and acceptance."*

Continue to tap until you feel a shift within yourself and give thanks for the healing. You may or may not share with the person that you have tapped for them. This practice can be very helpful and effective on planes or in crowds to share the peace and calming effects of tapping as well.

The Tapping Tree – Releasing the Past

I love working and playing with metaphors. One of my faves is the Tree of Life or the Tapping Tree. Our subconscious mind responds to imagery, so this can be a powerful healing process.

Get yourself a blank piece of paper and a pen and jump in with me.

Be sure to set aside some free time to move through this process.

Wrap yourself up in a blanket and have a warm cup of tea nearby.

We will be drawing a rough rendition of a tree on the paper and filling in the details, giving the tree a name and then tapping on the tree to relieve pain.

If it feels too scary to do this on your own, please ask for support and company.

Ready? Let's dive in.

1. In the middle of the paper - in the trunk - or on either side - very quickly list all the **things that have happened** with your body:

Accidents, illnesses, diagnoses, surgeries and anything else...

2. Then on the branches going up, write all of the negative **Emotions** associated with these events:

Sadness, fear, anxiety, frustration, guilt, regret, depression, etc.

3. Take a deep breath. Draw leaves on the branches and fill in the leaves with the **Symptoms** or **Side Effects**:

Insomnia, stiffness, tension, joint pain, exhaustion, illness, low energy...

4. Now draw the roots at the base of the tree. Fill in with **Limiting Beliefs & Fears** - about your body, about your health and your ability to heal:

What do you believe to be true? What is your self-talk? What about your future?

Breathe... Draw a big circle around your tree (you will be tearing it up and tossing or burning the paper!) and **give it a name**, such as:

This Terrible Tree - This Painful Tree - This Exhausting Tree

Set aside your paper and begin to Tap until you feel relief.

Set Up Statements:

"Even though I have this Painful Tree and part of me is holding on, for whatever reason, conscious or unconscious, I choose to relax and let go and open to the healing. I accept myself and all my feelings."

"Even though this Exhausting Tree is wearing me out, I accept myself and choose to release and let go."

Reminder Statements:

tapping around on the body points

"This painful tree…this painful tree…it's overwhelming. This painful tree…all the things that happened…all the feelings…all the symptoms…this painful tree, it's really holding me back. This painful tree… I can't let this stuff go, it's all too much!"

Checking In:

Take a deep breath, close your eyes and check in with your body. Notice your thoughts, emotions and physical sensations. Has the intensity come down some? Continue to tap until you feel relief.

You may also acknowledge (speak out loud perhaps) all of the items listed on the tree, as you continue to tap around on the body points.

Releasing Round:

Tapping on alternate body points.

"Feeling a bit calmer now…so much has happened…so many decisions… releasing the past… acknowledging my feelings… beginning to be willing to release and let go… allowing the energy to move…opening to the healing… releasing the past… allowing my body to heal…relaxing and letting go of the pain."

Give yourself permission to rest, nap, go for a walk and drink plenty of water. When you feel ready, enjoy tearing up the paper and tossing or burning it. Be gentle with yourself.

PART 5

Additional Information & Techniques

Clearing Food Cravings

"What tapping does incredibly well

is disrupt the fight-or-flight response,

Quickly allowing your body to return to a more relaxed state

in which it can digest food properly and support

healthier digestion and faster metabolism."

–Jessica Ortner, author of *The Tapping Solution for Weight Loss & Body Confidence*

Whether your goal is releasing excess weight or simply feeling better about your food choices and therefore feeling happier and more confident in your body, these simple practices may be helpful.

Because it's not about the food!

The foods we crave may very likely represent comfort, safety, fun or fulfillment in ways that we don't feel able to access in other, healthier ways. Be gentle and patient with yourself.

Perhaps eating comforting foods helps us prevent uncomfortable feelings or painful memories. That's where tapping helps us to acknowledge those memories and feelings and release the past, so that we can make healthy choices in the present.

Tapping To Reprogram Your Subconscious Mind

One of the simplest ways to relieve the struggle is to tap directly on the cravings, for example:

Set Up Statement:

"Even though I crave this chocolate, I accept myself and all my feelings and I choose to feel peaceful and calm."

Reminder Statements:

"I need this chocolate now. I need this chocolate…I have to have it now. This craving for chocolate…I need it now! This craving for chocolate… this intense craving...I can't focus on anything else!"

Tapping On the Underlying Feelings

When you are willing to gently explore what may lie beneath your cravings, practice noticing and being present with your feelings - before you reach for the food. I'm not saying this is easy to do. Acknowledging and releasing the past with relaxation and tapping can be very effective and help you to release the struggle and welcome change into your behavior.

Set Up Statement:

"Even though I crave this food to quiet my feelings, I accept myself and I am safe."

Reminder Statements:

"I need to eat this now. All these powerful feelings... I don't want to feel this. It's too much to handle, so I need this food. I don't feel safe. It's the only way I can get through this. All these feelings...It feels overwhelming."

Continue to tap until you feel relief from the intense feelings. Take a few deep breaths when you next feel the craving and tap before you act on the craving. Continue this practice each day as you continue to release and heal the past.

Complete your practice with Happy Tapping:

"I'm healing and releasing the past. I'm grateful for the healing. My body is my teacher. Feeling so much clearer now...Making healthy choices. ..I'm giving my body love and support. Feeling grateful for my strong, flexible, healthy body... Thank you, thank you, thank you!"

Decision Making With Ease

"The letter we all love to receive is one that carries so much of the writer's personality that she seems to be sitting beside us, looking at us directlyand talking just as she really would. Could she have come on a magic carpet, instead of sending her proxy in ink-made characters on mere paper?" Etiquette in Society, in Business, in Politics and at Home
by Emily Post, 1922

I strive to be a force for good in the world and wonder who remembers Emily Post? She was a writer, columnist and arbiter of good behavior from back in my grandmother's day. My beloved grandmother, Leah Katherine, who was a proper Victorian lady, taught me the Golden Rule - treat others as you would like to be treated. It has guided me all my life.

When it comes to making decisions, even the tough ones, do you settle for what is expected of you - or what you "should" be doing? Or do you trust your intuition and your own guidance?

Let's focus on decision making and utilize our Meditation & Tapping practice as our guide.

1. Recall an important decision that you need to make and ask the question. Then listen with your heart for the answer - **rather than listening with your head.**

   When making decisions about what is best for me to eat, my mouth wants things not good for my body. So now I notice what my mouth wants and then I pause and ask my body. My body almost always gives me a different and healthier answer.

My beloved husband, the engineer, says - "Pick one thing and do it - if it doesn't work out, try something else."

---

2. Remember you are always able to tap on the discomfort of not knowing. ***"Even though I can't make a decision right now, I deeply and completely love and accept myself."***

Give Your Critical Voice a New Job

All of us have experienced the nagging of our critical voice. My theory is that this is the function of the ego trying to keep us safe. It can be annoying, discouraging and persistent, I know.

And we are fully capable of **becoming more aware of the inner critic** and redirecting that conversation.

1. Begin by observing **what you are saying to yourself** inside your head all day long. Warning - this can be shocking!
2. Be grateful for the part of you that is keeping you safe. Pat your heart and say, ***"Thank you for keeping me safe - I've got this."***
3. Set an intention to catch yourself and **shift to a more positive**, encouraging thought.
4. **Be gentle with yourself** as you practice noticing what is going well in your day. We are reprogramming our minds

to pay more attention to what goes well and less attention to potential danger - **creating new neural pathways**.

5. Pause when you notice the critical voice. S**hift your awareness** to what feels good and savor that goodness for 10 seconds.
6. **Rinse and repeat**.

Let me know how you do with this practice. You can even practice when meditating - rather than struggling to quiet your mind.

Energization Exercises to Prepare for Meditation

I learned these wonderful energization exercises at The Expanding Light at Ananda in Nevada City, California (www.expandinglight.org) when I attended a month long Yoga Teacher Training in 1998. I have returned for personal retreat each year.

Paramhansa Yogananda, the well-known yoga master, created the Energization Exercises as a scientific and systematic method for increasing the flow of life-force and sending it to every area of the body in order to strengthen and energize it. These exercises also heal the body, clear and focus the mind and prepare you for meditation. Combining the double breath - double inhalation and double exhalation - with the tensing of each muscle in a wave: low, medium, high, then relaxing the muscle: high, medium, low, allows the conscious flow of energy throughout the body. A chart of all of the 39 exercises can be referenced at www.crystalclarity.com.

Double Breathing - Tense & Release –
Double inhale through the nose, tensing the body upward from the feet, with arms opening to the sides. Double exhale, relaxing the body downward. Repeat 3 - 5 times.

Single Arm Raising – Raise the right arm straight up while inhaling and tensing, relaxing the arm down while exhaling. Raise the left arm and repeat on each side three times.

Side to Side Stretch - Stretch the left arm over the head with feet slightly apart, tensing with double breath, then on right side, bending to the side at the waist. 3 times.

Medulla Massage - Finger tips of both hands on the base of the skull, massage in small circles, then lift the chin with a double breath in and tuck the chin exhaling. 3 times.

Skull Tapping - Gently tap all over your scalp with the fingertips of both hands.

Scalp Massage - Press the fingertips into the scalp and massage the scalp on the skull, moving the fingers around all over the scalp.

Whole Body Breathing
Bend over from the hips, pushing your sitting bones back behind you. Relax the entire body, especially the arms, neck and back. Double inhale as you smoothly bring your arms and torso back to the upright position, arms overhead, fully tensing the arms. Tense around the spine as you do this. Exhaling fully, relax back down. Do this three times.

Getting Unstuck

Have you been meditating, exercising, tapping and generally applying effort to your self-care and not seeing results?

Do you feel stuck? Frustrating, isn't it? It's not easy to change...

Every time I teach Meditation and Tapping, I explain that these practices are so effective for relaxation, stress relief and relief of acute pain.

More complex issues such as chronic pain, anxiety, weight loss, insomnia and grief can take much longer to resolve and we tend to resist change - even when we are seeking relief.

As much as we would like an easy fix, we often find that relief doesn't come soon enough for us. We practice for a few days or weeks and expect life-long issues to resolve. We may have experienced these conditions or held these beliefs for years, and we want solutions immediately, if not sooner.

When you are ready for a change:

1. Set an intention to practice meditation and tapping daily - even if only for a few minutes.

2. Be specific about the focus of your practice. Stick with it.

3. At first you might stay with acknowledging whatever you feel is holding you back - doubt, fear, frustration, anger, sadness, etc.
4. Be willing to release the past and change your self-talk.
5. Remember to tap through at least one alternate round - speaking to the issue and alternating on the points with choice statements. *"I'm ready to let this go… it's time to let this go…it's safe to let this go…I'm relaxing and letting go."*

Giving Thanks for the Healing

I want to encourage you to continue to practice, watch instructional videos, read books and practice with friends or in a class.

When I feel stuck I find that I'm just about to shift to a new level of experience. Don't give up on your ability to heal, learn and grow.

Be patient with yourself and others…

Lovingkindness Practice

Link to Lovingkindness chanting video:
https://www.youtube.com/watch?v=WzNO-NiYOSQ&t=5s

The Pali or Sanskrit word for lovingkindness is *metta.*, sometimes translated simply as "love." We often speak of love, but "lovingkindness" is a less familiar term to most of us. Typically, the word love conjures up thoughts of passion, which is associated with attachment, wanting, owning, and possessing. This is actually a state of great fear and anxiety, which is a conditional offering. In contract, the spirit of *metta* is like a freely offered gift. Like water pouring from one vessel to another, it flows freely, taking the shape of each situation without changing its essence. If somebody disappoints you or fails to meet your expectations, your feeling of lovingkindness can still remain. By the same token, your lovingkindness toward yourself need not be destroyed when you feel, as we all do sometimes, that you have let yourself down.

It is said that the Buddha first taught *metta* meditation as an antidote to fear. According to legend, he sent a group of monks to meditate in a forest that was inhabited by tree spirits. The tree spirits resented the monks' presence, so they decided to scare them away. The monks fled the forest, begging, "Please, Lord Buddha, send us to meditate in some other forest." The Buddha said, "I'm going to send you back to the very same forest – but this time, I'll give you the only protection you need." He then taught them to recite the phrases and to do the heartfelt practice of lovingkindness. It is said that the monks returned to the forest and practiced *metta*. The tree spirits were so moved by the energy of lovingkindness that they decided to serve and protect the monks.

The practice of lovingkindness relies on our ability to open continuously to the truth of our actual experience, not cutting off the painful parts and not trying to pretend things are other than they are. Our minds are open and expansive; spacious enough to contain all the pleasures and pains of a life fully lived. Pain is part of the reality of human experience and an opportunity for us to practice maintaining our authentic presence.

The Buddha taught that the mental forces that bring suffering can temporarily obstruct positive forces like love or wisdom, but they can never destroy them. Love is a greater power than fear or anger or guilt, so it has the capacity to undo painful mind states. The manifestations of our mental conditioning challenge us to see them for what they are and to remember our own true nature. *We come back to our natural radiance and the purity of our minds by experiencing metta.*

Loving others without any love for ourselves tramples on healthy boundaries, leading to what we call "codependency." We spend our lives searching painfully and fruitlessly for intimacy. Yet we have only to contact our own true nature in order to experience the natural radiance and purity of our minds. That's the beginning of being able to extend lovingkindness toward all beings everywhere. It's also an essential requirement for experiencing the quality of love we all so deeply want to give and receive. In Buddhist psychology, *metta* is identified as the cohesive factor in consciousness. Metta brings all beings together. Love moistens the heart, so that it can join with others in an authentic expression of connectedness.

Benefits of Lovingkindness:

You sleep well while enjoying pleasant dreams and awaken easily. People love you and celestial beings (*devas*) love and protect you. You are safe from external dangers. Your face is radiant and your mind serene. You will be unconfused at the moment of death and take rebirth in the higher, happier realms.

The Phrases of Metta:

If these phrases do not touch your heart, come up with your own. The important thing is to use words that are meaningful to you.

May I be free from danger. May I be happy. May I be healthy. May I live with ease.

May you be free from danger. May we be free from danger.

Or another version of this practice, which has been turned into a well-known chant:

May I be filled with lovingkindness. May I be well. May I be peaceful and at ease and may I be happy. May you be filled with lovingkindness. May we be filled with lovingkindness…

The Practice of Metta:

The traditional practice uses a series of phrases directed in order to yourself, to someone you find inspiring, or to whom you feel grateful. Next, move on to a beloved friend and then on to a person you may encounter in your daily life who is neutral or you don't know well. Now you are ready to send lovingkindness to someone with whom you have had difficulty or conflict. Doing this practice does not mean you are excusing their behavior, rather, you are engaging in the marvelous process of discovering and cultivating your inherent capacity for unconditional love. Directing metta toward a difficult person leads to the discovery of your own capacity for lovingkindness that is born of freedom. In the final phase of the practice, we move on to offer metta to all beings everywhere, without distinction or exception.

Adapted from *Insight Meditation Workbook* by Sharon Salzberg & Joseph Goldstein

Matrix Reimprinting – Going Deeper with EFT

"EFT is a self-help tool that is used to resolve or improve physical or emotional issues, destructive thought patterns or forms of behavior. It involves tapping on points along the body's meridian system - the system used in acupuncture. While tapping on the points, you bring to mind physical symptoms or negative memories. This helps to release life stresses or physical issues from the body and allows it to return to emotional and physical health."

–Karl Dawson & Sasha Allenby in *Matrix Reimprinting Using EFT*

I often turn to my collection of books on EFT and found the quote above with a terrific description of how EFT works for healing.

You may already have experienced the amazing healing benefits of EFT for immediate pain relief, stress relief and relaxation.

If you have yet to experience EFT tapping, please view this video I've created to introduce the Basic Recipe technique.

Should you be ready to deepen your practice a bit, I would like to share with you another powerful way to practice EFT for healing.

EFT to heal a memory from the past:

As always, allow yourself some **quiet time to get settled**, do some stretches and practice deep breathing. Once you feel centered, grounded and connected to your intuition and inner wisdom, ask:

1. **"Please guide me to a memory that will help me heal."**
2. Accept whatever comes up to be healed.
3. Create a **simple Set Up phrase** to begin your tapping practice.
4. **Example:** *"Even though I have this memory of leaving home at 18, I choose to love and accept myself, just as I am."*
5. Tap on the side of both hands while repeating this Set Up statement and remember to **use your own words**.
6. Allow yourself to **connect with your younger self** - how you felt, the circumstances of the memory and how this may have played out throughout your life.
7. **Powerful Question:** *What did you decide about life then?*
8. Now you may tap on this limiting belief:
9. **Example:** *"Even though I decided I was not good enough, I now choose to release this limiting belief with love and acceptance. I love and accept myself, just as I am, and I am safe."*

10. Continue to tap around on the body points with the thoughts, emotions and sensations that arise until you feel relief. Be very gentle with yourself.

Important Note: If deep and disturbing memories arise, please get in touch with a Practitioner to support you. Do not practice this on your own. It is OK to ask for help.

---

11. You may complete your practice session by **speaking in your heart to your younger self** to assure them that they are loved, that you are always with them and that all is well now.

This practice will provide **powerful healing and release** from even life-long concerns and conditions.

You may deepen the learning by **writing about what you have learned** and visit your younger self in your daily practice to anchor the new feelings of love, connection and understanding.

Personal Peace Process with EFT

The Personal Peace Process, developed by Gary Craig, involves making a list of every troublesome specific event and systematically tapping on each one. As you neutralize and eliminate the internal conflict, you relieve emotional and physical suffering.

When you begin the process by making the list, you are already half way there, in my experience. As you begin to tap on each item on the list, with an intention to relieve the intensity of the baggage and release the past, the whole bundle may be lifted from your shoulders.

1. Make a time line of your life in segments, i.e. zero to five, six to ten years old, etc.
2. List the troublesome or painful events you can remember, beginning with the big ones. The smaller ones may fade away easily. Include relationships, illnesses, accidents, deaths or moves in a few words each.

3. Note the emotional intensity of each item on a scale of 0 - 10.
4. Set aside quiet time to tap on the highest intensity items on your list. Using your own words as you tap, include the emotions that arise for you. You may tap on one or two items per day. Be gentle with yourself. Tap until you feel relief.
5. Add anything new to the list that arises as you are tapping.
6. Each time you practice, end your session with positive or gratitude tapping - "*I'm so grateful for the healing...*" *I'm ready to let this go.*" "*I am safe.*"
7. Notice how you are feeling physically and emotionally over the days and weeks as you practice. Write about what you notice.
8. My experience with this practice is that I began to feel much lighter, clearer, more relaxed and joyful quite soon.
9. Please be gentle with yourself. This process may bring up painful memories and intense feelings. You may want to ask for support and company from a friend, counselor, EFT practitioner or trusted family member.

Releasing & Healing the Past

Of all the methods and practices I've shared over the years, I believe that the willingness to release the past is the key to profound and lasting healing. We absolutely cannot change the past, as much as we would like to sometimes. Our subconscious minds automatically replay past hurts and traumas to protect us. The good news is that we can retrain our minds to shift our focus from the past to the present.

EFT tapping is the simplest and most effective way to acknowledge and release the past that I know. EFT accesses a different part of the brain than talk therapy and allows us to become conscious of our habits, patterns, and limiting beliefs and fears.

Take a deep breath and choose a painful memory that you would like to release. Notice the feelings that arise, physically and emotionally. Trust that you will be guided to the perfect memory for your healing at this time. Tap to release the stuck feelings or simply tap while you tell the story about what happened.

Set Up Statement:

Even though I can't stop thinking about this (insult/injury/betrayal/disappointment), part of me is holding on, for whatever reason, conscious or unconscious. I now choose to release and let go of the past, with love and acceptance. I love, accept and forgive myself and everyone else involved. I am safe."

Reminder Statements:

(Use your own words as you tap around on the body points, until you feel relief.)

"This old story…so much pain…I still feel hurt and resentful. This deep pain and hurt…I'm still so angry. All this anger and resentment…can't let this go. There's sadness too…can't let this go. Part of me is holding on…can't let this go. So much pain, anger and resentment…"

Please be gentle with yourself as you open to the healing, forgiveness and release. Set an intention to be open and willing to allow your feelings to flow and your body to release the holding. **Always end your practice with gratitude and happy tapping:** *"I am so grateful for the healing. I'm grateful for my willingness to forgive. I'm grateful for all of the blessings in my life. Thank you, thank you, thank you."*

PART 6

Self-Care

Deepening Your Practice with Healthy Boundaries

Many of you may be reading about Meditation and EFT and/or attending classes and not yet practicing on your own at home. I want to encourage you to find the time - even a few minutes per day - and make the intention to stretch, breathe and sit quietly to calm your nervous system and come into alignment.

Attending a class or a group where you are able to learn and practice with others is a great way to integrate the healing practices into your daily life. That's when you will truly begin to see results.

With all of the chaos that is arising in our world, we need all the help we can get to stay centered, grounded and present.

Suggestions:

- Please minimize how much you watch and read the news.

- Drink plenty of water throughout the day to stay hydrated.
- Begin your day with a simple centering practice, such as deep breathing and energization exercises.
- Complete your day with progressive relaxation and gratitude before sleep.
- Ask for protection around your heart and around your body. You might visualize healing light and gently pulse the edges until you feel comfortable, safe and relaxed.
- Then send loving kindness to all of those in need, nearby and far away. See them receiving love, support and all the comfort that they need.

In your quiet time, you may also notice your internal and external boundaries.

Practice this for a few minutes each day or whenever you feel impacted by the events around you. Be gentle with yourself.

EFT setup phrases to help you stay calm and centered:

While tapping the karate chop spots on the side of both hands, repeat these phrases out loud, (or use your own words).

"Even though there is so much chaos in the world and I'm really feeling affected by it all, I choose to center myself in love and acceptance."

"Even though I'm feeling sad about all that is happening in the world, I acknowledge these feelings and center myself in love and I am safe."

Now for the phrases that focus on the circumstances - while tapping around on the body points:

"Feeling so sad about all that is happening in the world...All this sadness and grief...These feelings are overwhelming. All this sadness...I don't know how to respond. I accept myself and all my feelings. Practice healthy boundaries... Centering myself in love... Bringing myself back to my center...Acknowledging my feelings...I have the ability to stay in the present moment."

Pranayama Breathing Practices

Breathing In Joy, Strength & Courage

Whenever you feel worried or scattered, try breathing in not just air but joy, peace, strength and courage – breathe in whatever positive quality you'd like to experience. Imagine the breath filling your entire body, not just your lungs. Hold the breath for a comfortable time while focusing at the point between the eyebrows. As you exhale strongly, expel any worry or confusion.

Full Yogic Breath

When we are able to breathe more fully, we tend to feel stronger and more expansive in our outlook. Practice the Full Yogic Breath while standing or sitting:

1. Begin by sweeping your arms and hands up and fully expanding the breath in the diaphragm.
2. Consciously expand the ribs and sides of the body.

3. Then bring the breath up around the heart and into the upper chest.
4. Release the breath while bending forward and sweeping the arms and hands down. Tuck the chin and relax and back of the neck. Listen to your body and find your own pace, following your breath. Repeat several times to enrich your capacity for Joy.

Measured Breathing

This is a simple breathing technique to begin your meditation practice and quiet your mind. Settle yourself down and lengthen your spine to allow for breath and energy to flow freely. Close your eyes, if you like. Breathe through your nose, if your nose is clear, otherwise breathe through your mouth. Inhale for a count of seven, hold the breath for seven and exhale for seven. Repeat several times and then allow your breathing to relax and flow naturally.

Breath connects us to life and to higher consciousness.

Rituals for Self-Love

Mindfulness practice is not simply helpful for our meditation periods. Mindfulness throughout the day allows us to live in the moment more fully and vastly improve our health and wellbeing.

Some benefits of mindfulness practice are:

- Better memory
- Improved mood
- Better sleep
- Lower blood pressure and blood sugar
- Balanced hormones
- Improved immunity
- Fewer headaches
- Pain relief

We are all creatures of habit. We have our routines and ways that we function in daily life. From time to time it might be good to pay closer attention to those routines and how they are serving our health and wellbeing.

Ask yourself:

How mindful am I when I am getting ready for the day?
How aware am I of my tendency to push myself?
When I am tired, how do I slow down and rest?
Am I fully present with my loved ones when we are together?

Allow plenty of time to prepare your breakfast this morning. Preparing food can be a loving ritual of nourishment for your body.

> *Give yourself the gift of MINDFULNESS as a self-love practice.*

Slow down and ask what would taste good, not necessarily what is convenient. Perhaps taking a few extra minutes to prepare oatmeal with fresh fruit and nuts will be more appealing that dry cereal.

- Enjoy the ritual of brewing a cup of tea with lemon and honey.
- Sit quietly to savor your food, rather than munching on the fly.
- See if you can maintain your Mindfulness throughout the day.

Notice when you feel tired and need to rest. Stop and take a deep breath at red lights when you are driving. Design a ritual for bed time that includes a warm bath, a bit of journaling, a brief meditation to give thanks for all that went well during your day

Simple EFT First Aid:

1. When you feel stressed or witness anything stressful, tap on the top of your head, where many of the meridian points come together. This will keep you from taking in the trauma.

2. In the car, in a meeting, or when you want to be discreet - tap the tips of your fingers together with both hands and breathe...

3. Interlace the tips of your fingers on both hands to stimulate the meridian points on the sides of each finger nail.

4. Pat your heart and take three deep breaths.

Remember to set aside a few uninterrupted minutes to settle down and take a few deep breaths with your eyes closed, before you begin tapping.

Check in with your body. Notice where your attention goes. Create a simple Set-Up statement about the issue or condition you would like to focus on for your healing session.

Combination Set Up Statement and Reversal -

speaking to the subconscious resistance to change:

While tapping on the karate chop spots:

"*Even though I'm uncomfortable, part of me doesn't want to tell the truth about this, for whatever reason, conscious or unconscious, I deeply and completely accept myself anyway.*"

"*Even though I feel unhappy, for whatever reason, conscious or unconscious, I've felt this way for so long, I now choose to love, accept and forgive myself, just as I am.*"

Tap around on the ten body points:

All this discomfort…not sure what's wrong with me. All this discomfort… There's always something! Not sure what's causing this… always pushing myself to get more done. Can't slow down and relax. I acknowledge this discomfort and what my body is telling me. It's not safe to let this go. I don't deserve to rest and play. All this discomfort in my body…I'd like to let this energy move. Not safe to take time for myself…

> *Especially with complex issues and long-standing patterns, be gentle with yourself and tap to calm your anxiety and ask for support for the big deal issues.*

Be as specific as possible with your set-up statements. Follow the shifting aspects as they arise. Trust your intuition and body wisdom.

When you begin to feel relief and have neutralized your issue, do at least one more round of ***positive tapping***:

I'm so grateful for this clarity. I feel better already. I'm able to see a more positive approach. I'm willing to relax and enjoy my day. I'm so grateful for all of the blessings in my life. I am open to new solutions. I'm willing to ask for help and guidance. Thank you for my strong, flexible, healthy body.

Your intuition and body wisdom may give you some clarity about how to heal and release the discomfort. Namaste'

Tapping for Caregivers

All of us at one time or another become caregivers, whether we are parents caring for children, adults caring for our parents, or adults caring for siblings, friends or neighbors. There is a special place in my heart for caregivers because I've been there myself several times. We are faced with big challenges, decisions and a flood of emotions, such as sadness, fear, and anxiety, not to mention the stress of responsibility for someone else's well-being.

Set Up Statements:

"Even though I have all these responsibilities and it's exhausting, I love and accept myself and all my feelings."

"Even though I feel frustrated and overwhelmed and part of me is holding onto these feelings, for whatever reason, conscious or unconscious, I choose to relax and take care of myself with love and acceptance."

Reminder Statements:

"All this responsibility…So much to do and so little time. All this pressure…So many details…It feels like it's all up to me. I feel exhausted. So many decisions…It's just too much."

When You Begin to Feel Relief

Set Up Statement:

"Even though I feel calmer and more relaxed, part of me might still be holding on to the stress, for whatever reason, conscious or unconscious. I choose to remember my needs and I love, accept and forgive myself and I am safe."

Reminder Statements:

"This remaining stress and overwhelming…I'd really like to let it go. This remaining frustration…It's time to release it now. The truth is I'm doing the best I can. This remaining sadness and regret…It's safe to relax and let go. Any remaining pressure that I'm putting on myself, I am beginning to release and let go."

Continue to tap until you feel relief from the intense feelings. Take a few deep breaths whenever you feel fatigue and anxiety. Continue this practice each day as you continue to practice taking good care of yourself as well as your loved ones.

Complete your practice with Happy Tapping:

"I can handle this. I'm grateful for the healing. I'm listening to my body. I'm feeling so much clearer now. I'm making healthy choices. I'm giving my body love and support. It's safe to ask for help. I don't need to do all of this by myself. I'm grateful for my strong, flexible, healthy body. Thank you, thank you, thank you!"

I love and approve of myself. I am safe.

Ultimate Truth Statement

Using EFT to Reach and Maintain Your Ideal Weight

Over 60% of our population is overweight. One out of three women and one out of four men are on a diet at any given time. Why is that? Why do we eat when we're not even hungry? Why aren't people more successful when trying to lose weight? And why do we quickly put it back on if we do manage to lose some?

Weight is a Symptom – Why do you weigh more than you want to or think you should weigh? And no, it's not just because you overeat. That is a symptom. Part of this process is discovering and neutralizing the cause for your weight gain.

This is a simple step-by-step program that really works, without dieting. But it will only work, if you actually Do It. Just reading about it won't make you skinny. I promise. Following these steps will help you reach your desired goal.

Here's the Secret - Losing weight is about reaching your target weight and focusing on all of the motivations and reasons to be there. ***It's not about losing weight***! It's that focus on how you will feel when you reach your goal that will keep you on track.

1. Identify your weight goal, how much you ideally want to weigh (rather than how much you want to lose.) This is an important distinction because shifting your focus to what you want can entirely shift your experience. Yay!
2. Identify why you want to lose weight (i.e. to improve my health, to be thinner for my daughter's wedding, or my 25th reunion, or our trip to Hawaii, etc.) Expound on that.
3. Add more reasons and benefits.
4. Write down the emotions you would expect to experience when you reach your target weight – such as happiness, pride, confidence, certainty, joy, peace of mind, comfort, improved self-esteem.
5. Write some of the reasons your subconscious might NOT want you to lose weight: I won't feel safe, my clothes will no longer fit, I don't want others to notice me, what if I fail? etc. Be as honest with yourself as possible.
6. Now, do a tapping reversal on those reasons:

Tap on your karate chop points while saying: *"Even though I DON'T want to weigh ____ pounds (fill in your ideal weight) for whatever reason, conscious or unconscious, I love and accept myself anyway."* Do this three times. This very important step helps to acknowledge the subconscious resistance to change.

Write a simple **Ultimate Truth Statement** (a first person, present tense goal) about reaching your target weight, including the reasons, benefits and emotions of how you will feel when you reach your target weight.

Example:

> *"I am happy, excited and healthy weighing 160 pounds. I feel confident and self-assured seeing myself looking great, feeling great and having more energy. And I am totally committed to maintaining this new-found health and vitality."*

Stay focused only on the positive. The Ultimate Truth Statement is your goal, your contract with yourself. Now decide where you are on the 1 to 10 scale in being able to say the statement with confidence. You can see and feel yourself already there.

Now that you know where you are you can identify the discrepancy between where you are now and where you want to be. You must clear up any limiting beliefs or fears that are in your way. We will now work on **the underlying cause for the weight problem, and the resistance to reaching your goal**.

Assign an intensity level to these issues: fear, being teased as a child, low self-esteem, limiting beliefs and fears, etc.

Neutralize the resistance with a **Reversal**. Tapping three times on the karate chop point – *"Even though I don't want to let go of these fears about losing weight, I love and accept myself anyway."*

Tap for three rounds on the body points with each fear or childhood issue until they are clear. This can take some time. Be gentle with yourself.

Use the **Choice Method** when the intensity begins to come down below a 5: *"Even though I still have some fear of losing weight, I now choose to begin to let this go."*

Return to the **Ultimate Truth Statement** and tap on that, releasing any remaining fears that arise until you are able to say the UTS with complete confidence. Continue practicing the UTS every day until you have achieved your ideal weight and beyond.

Make achieving and staying at your ideal weight a life choice, so that eating healthy and being healthy becomes your way of life. Make your Ultimate Truth Statement a commitment and your contract with yourself. Choose to make it easy to honor it.

Ultimate Truth Statement for Abundance

The Ultimate Truth Statement is a powerful tapping tool to empower your affirmations and is especially effective with abundance issues or to focus on achieving your goals. It is NOT recommended for complex issues, serious illness or trauma.

1. Write a simple **description of your goal**, such as increasing income, new job, home or relationship.
2. Describe **how life will be** when you have achieved this goal using powerful, positive and present-tense wording.
3. Describe **how you will feel** as you move toward and attain this goal.
4. Add statements of **gratitude and simplicity** to your statement
5. Rate your **believability** or ownership of your statement on a scale of 1 – 10 with 10 being you have complete confidence in your ability to fulfill this goal. (This is opposite to your usual EFT rating where you look at the intensity of your issue.)
6. Identify any **blocks or obstacles** in your way – fears, limiting beliefs, safety issues, past baggage, resistance, worthiness, punishment, disapproval, reversals, need to figure out how, sabotage, revenge.
7. **Bundle these obstacles** – give the bundle a name and tap through the points to acknowledge and release these obstacles.
8. P**sychological Reversal** – *"Even though I don't want to let go of this resistance, I love and accept myself and all of my feelings."*
9. Tap away each of your individual obstacles and blockages.
10. When obstacles are down to a zero, reassess your UTS.

11. **Trouble Shoot** – Tap on alternate points with any remaining resistance – *"This remaining resistance…I choose to let this go. This remaining obstacle…I release and I let go."*

12. Identify what is **holding you back** from completely realizing your Ultimate Truth Statement. *"I choose to release any remaining obstacles (fears or beliefs) keeping me from owning my UTS."*

13. 13. Tap on your UTS **twice per day** to stay focused on your goals and keep you in the vibration to receive your desired results.

Ultimate Truth Statement – Summary

1. Write your Ultimate Truth Statement and rate it 0 – 10 on how true you feel it is for you right now.
2. Identify fears and beliefs standing in your way.
3. Bundle the obstacles.
4. Do a Reversal Neutralization on the obstacles and blockages.
5. Tap away the obstacles – remembering to be gentle with yourself.
6. Go back and reassess your Ultimate Truth Statement.
7. If not a 10 (fully true for you), trouble shoot until you own the UTS fully.
8. Tap on your UTS twice per day for several weeks.
9. Enjoy your results!

Visioning Guided Meditation

The purpose of Visioning Guided Meditation is to open a place in our consciousness for fresh ideas to be revealed. We center ourselves in the silence, establish awareness of the Divine within and open to inner wisdom, intuition and guidance.

Visions may appear in the form of images, colors, sounds or feelings. At times nothing may be revealed. We accept whatever comes or doesn't come without judgment, knowing that more will be revealed.

The questions:

1. **What is the HIGHEST VISION for my life/health/career?**
2. **What must I RELEASE to fulfill this vision** - what am I releasing or forgiving that no longer serves me?

NOTE: This is the perfect time to utilize your **EFT tapping** practice to acknowledge and release whatever wants to be released or forgiven so that you can move forward.

3. **What must I EMBRACE** to fulfill this vision? What am I welcoming into my experience?

4. **What must I BE** for this vision to be fulfilled? What qualities will support me in this transformation and growth?

5. **How can I take INSPIRED ACTION** to fulfill this vision?

6. **Give Thanks** for the Vision, for the guidance, for the opportunity to connect with your intuition, body wisdom and Divine guidance.

Following your meditation you may record your insights in your journal and/or share the vision with a trusted friend or coach, who will help you affirm your greater good.

Here is one of my Visioning meditation sessions, to inspire you to join me in this amazing practice. I copied this right out of my journal:

Vision - *In a meadow, most glorious, with nothing allergenic - sunshine, perfect temp, little breeze, flowers and trees, Disney butterflies, a stream running over rocks. It's not just my spot; it's irresistible to everyone else. They all want to come here to play with me. Coming into this space opens people's hearts. A place they find themselves, what they're looking for within themselves. Find other people to play with. It's utterly safe. It's a place that calls forth possibility. People want to be part of the solution here. They want to connect here. It's very open. People can come and go freely. We bring our best selves to this circle. There's a feeling beyond everything being possible; everyone can have what they want here. Together everything can be solved.*

Release - *"Nobody wants to play with me. Really clear... loneliness... I don't know how to do it, create community, invite people. Doubt...No matter what I do, it isn't good enough. Will this work? Will this sustain me?*

Embrace: *Fun, big fun! Nature. Beauty. Community. Creativity. Learning. Teaching. Traveling. Collaboration. More fun. Music.*

Somehow my photography is in there. Adventure. Generosity. Worthiness. Excellence. Success. Joy. Celebration. Lots of people to play with. I get the image of dropping a pebble in the water and the rings expanding out, out, out. Natural expansion that's effortless, easy, joyful. Dancing in the moment.

Being - *Strong. Healthy. Confident. Joyful. Playful. Excited. Welcoming. Creative. Adventurous. Grateful. Peaceful. Curious. Content.*

Gratitude *lives in my body and in my heart.*
May this guided meditation connect you with your intuition and Divine guidance and move you forward with clarity, confidence and enthusiasm!

Feeling Guilty When You Take Time Off to Relax and Play

> *The good news is that you can uncover the negative patterns and change them.*

When I launched my photography business, 30 years ago, I didn't have a clue about work/life balance. I didn't hear the term until years later.

I threw myself into the business and loved every minute of it. I worked in my home office, marketing and doing paperwork all week long, and then went out to photograph weddings and families on the weekends.

And I did that for 15 years until my body gave out and I was forced to slow down.

Gradually I learned to take Fridays off and one week of vacation each year. I still vividly remember the first time we landed in Hawaii and stepped off the plane. Now that's a great place to relax!

Eventually I learned that it was challenging for me to relax at home, because I worked from a home office. I could really relax when we went to the ocean or away on a trip.

The physical and emotional collapse taught me the hard way - how to slow down and rest. Even now when I take time off to rest and play, I still feel guilty sometimes, as if it's not OK to stop working.

Giving yourself permission to relax takes practice. You may need to ease into it slowly.

- Take part of a day off and see how that feels.
- Take a full day off and see how you do.
- Schedule a weekend, without work, only fun!
- Work your way up to a week away to relax & play.

This past holiday season I allowed myself two full weeks off from teaching and coaching and it felt great. I felt a big difference in my level of enjoyment and ease.

Things will not fall apart while you are unplugged - I promise. And you can always Meditate & Tap on the anxiety, guilt and doubt that you feel about not working and let go of the worry, fear and tension

Another Approach to Healing the Past

"No matter what happened to you - or how long ago it happened –you must do the healing work that only you can do.

Failure to do so just perpetuates pain and dis-ease."

–Christiane Northrup, M.D.

In her marvelous book, "Goddesses Never Age", Dr. Northrop offers dozens of practices for release and relief of the past, to allow the emotions to flow gently and freely:

- Watch a sad movie - Anne Hathaway singing "I Dreamed a Dream" in *Les Miserable* and allow yourself to weep.
- Release anger, resentment, fear and disappointment by writing a letter to express your feelings and then tear up or burn the letter. (You need never speak of this with anyone.)

- Go to the ocean or a lake, meditate and write the essence of your feelings on a stone and toss it into the water. *"You're probably going to be a ruddy, honking, snorting, sobbing wet mess of raw emotion, and so what? Let it out, release those emotions."*

I love Dr. Northup's sense of humor and her compassion as well. We all know that holding onto the past is not helpful.

Let's explore a simple and effective tapping practice (including meditation) to open to forgiveness and peace of mind. We feel resentment when someone else has hurt us or betrayed us, we feel regret when we feel back about something we have done.

1. Settle yourself down where you won't be disturbed for twenty to thirty minutes. Have a journal or paper and pen handy.
2. Take a few deep cleansing breaths, releasing the breath with a sigh. Ahhhh...
3. Center yourself in the present moment and surround your body with unconditional love and light. Focus on your breath as you gradually relax your body from head down to your toes.
4. Gently turn your attention inward and connect with your intuition and body wisdom. Open to your guidance and infinite wisdom.
5. Ask to be guided to a situation where you still feel upset with yourself.
6. Trust wherever your guidance leads you and be open to healing.
7. Take a few minutes to write about this situation - including the circumstances, the thoughts, emotions and memories. Notice how intense thinking about this feels in your body.

Set Up Statement:

"Even though this happened and I can't forgive myself for what happened, I deeply and completely love, honor and accept myself and all my feelings."

"Even though I can't let this go, part of me is holding on, for whatever reason, conscious or unconscious, I choose to be willing to acknowledge and release with love and acceptance, for myself and everyone else involved."

NOTE: Remember to use your own words and be as specific as possible with your statement.

Reminder Statements:

Eyebrow points: *I'm upset with myself for ...*
Side of eyes: *I feel bad that I ...*
Under eyes: *I was wrong to ...*
Under nose: *Feeling so bad about ...*
Under mouth: *I'd really like to be able to let this go ...*
Collarbones: (deep breath) *I'm afraid this will happen again*
Under arms: *I feel so stupid*
Ribs: *Feels impossible to let this go*
Wrists: *Wishing I could do it differently*
Top of head: *It's time to let this go.*

Pause and check in with yourself - your thoughts, feelings, sensations. What do you notice?

The first round is designed to **acknowledge the issue**, then you can begin to make Choice Statements to release and forgive yourself.

Take your time with this. You are telling the truth and giving yourself permission to let go of the past - to forgive yourself so that you can learn from your mistakes and move forward.

Choice Statements:

"I now choose to release the past. I choose to relax and let go. It's time to release this regret. I'm allowing the energy to move. Choosing to move forward with love and acceptance... It's safe to let this go . I've learned so much. I forgive myself for all that I have done. Can't change the past...I choose to open to the healing. Accepting and asking for guidance...Releasing and letting go in every cell in my body...

Complete your healing session with gratitude Meditation and Tapping. Giving thanks for the guidance, the healing and the strength and clarity to move on with love and acceptance.

Centering & Quieting Your Wandering Mind

Link To Tapping Video: https://www.youtube.com/watch?v=IuxNMGUEYv4&t=120s

I've had conversations recently about challenges with quieting the mind for meditation.

Somehow we think it will be easy to center ourselves and be quiet - resting our bodies and minds. That is not always the case, as you may have noticed.

I've heard from my students that they are able to settle when we practice together in class or in a private session and not so much on their own.

There is a definite benefit to practicing with a group or with a teacher to guide you. That is how I learned to meditate and that's why I love to teach and practice with a group.

Here are some simple tools to help you with your meditation practice at home. Find what works well for you.

Be patient as you integrate the practice into your schedule - even for a few minutes each day. You will enjoy greater mental focus and clarity, ease, calm, peace of mind and relaxation.

The test of your success in meditation is not whether you have visions, but rather how you are changing as a person in everyday life. Are you becoming a happier person? The goal is to have your whole life become a meditation.

Reprograming Your Subconscious Mind

Set Up Statement:

"Even though I have all of this negative self-talk, and part of me is holding on to these old patterns, I want love and accept myself anyway."

Reminder Statements:

"All this negative self-talk…It's so discouraging. No matter how much I try, can't seem to change these thoughts. It's really holding me back. All this negative self-talk… Where did it come from? I'd really like to let this go. All this critical self-talk…"

Tapping On the Negative Thoughts

When you are willing to gently explore and notice your self-talk, you will become more aware of the programming from your family, your teachers, your culture.

This programming is embedded in our subconscious minds. Our subconscious minds are designed to protect us from danger - so we automatically focus on the negative.

Set Up Statement:

"Even though this negative self-talk is weighing me down, I choose to acknowledge these patterns with love and acceptance."

Reminder Statements:

"Noticing my inner dialog…I'm willing to forgive myself. Maybe this is something I can practice. A little bit at a time. I am capable of reprogramming my thoughts. Practicing patience…Observing my thoughts… Creating new neural pathways… A little bit every day…"

Continue to tap until you feel relief from the frustration and negativity. Take a few deep breaths when you notice the inner critic and tap before you move into being hard on yourself. Continue this practice each day as you continue to release and heal the past.

Complete your practice with Happy Tapping:

"I'm healing and releasing the past. I'm grateful for the healing. Reprogramming my subconscious mind… I'm feeling so much clearer now. Making healthy choices… I'm giving my body love and support. I'm grateful for my strong, flexible, healthy body. Thank you, thank you, thank you, thank you!"

Self-Care Guidelines

Wellbeing Practices – No Matter What!

1. **Sip warm, juicy water all day long** – We are all running around dehydrated without realizing it. Sipping water throughout the day, rather than coffee, soda or juice, will help to clear and calm your mind and body. Room temperature or warm water with a little juice in it is easier to absorb than ice cold water.

2. **Awareness of your breath** – Whenever you feel tired, stressed or anxious – stop! Close your eyes if convenient, and take a few slow deep breaths. This also will calm your mind and your body.

3. **Awareness of your thoughts** – Is your mind zooming from one task to the next or filled with worry and hurrying? Practice focusing in the present moment. Observe thoughts of the past or the future and come back to this moment. This is called Mindfulness practice – simple and profound.

4. **Healthier food choices** – Lifestyle choices that you are able to sustain. Less sugar – more fruit. Less caffeine – more

water. Less meat – more vegetables. Here's my favorite green smoothie recipe: 1-1/2 – 2 cups of water, cut up an apple or banana, 2 large leaves of chard or kale (without the hard stems), a handful of mixed greens, ½ cup blueberries or pineapple chunks, one tablespoon of flax or coconut oil. Yum!

5. **Rest and Sleep** – Do you consistently get less than six hours of sleep per night? For one week try going to bed one hour earlier. Turn off the TV, don't eat before going to bed, give yourself some quiet time to give thanks and release the day. Keep your bedroom quiet, clean and only for resting, making love and sleeping. See how this improves your waking hours. When you are tired – rest! Really – you have my permission.

If this is too much all at once – choose one practice and try if for 30 days, and let me know how it works for you. The good news is that these practices are all things you are able to do for yourself all day throughout the day – no matter what! This simple awareness will improve your physical and emotional health, mental clarity and well-being.

When you feel ready to try a few more:

1. Reduce the amount of TV, radio, newspapers, magazines and internet you consume, especially the news before bedtime.
2. Clear the clutter from you home, office, car and yard. It is truly amazing how much energy our stuff takes up!
3. **Get moving** – Our bodies are designed to move. If you are not enjoying at least some exercise every other day, find someone to walk with at lunch time, ride a bike, go dancing, walk the dog, take a yoga or spin class. It doesn't matter what you do so long as you enjoy it and you do it consistently. You will sleep better, have more energy, make wiser food choices and smile more, I promise.

Overcoming Resistance to Change – Examining Limiting Beliefs

"As much pain as negative beliefs can cause, we aren't always taught to evaluate them. Whether we adopted them from our immediate environment or they were passed down to us from our parents, they often appear disguised as facts. As we get older we tend to settle into beliefs and think what we believe is just how the world is - and, more dangerously. This is just who I am."

–Jessica Ortner, author of *The Tapping Solution for Weight Loss & Body Confidence*

We all have stories we tell ourselves about who we are and how we are.

What is your story?

Do you find yourself struggling to start a new activity or continue once you've started? Do you procrastinate about daily self-care and chores.

I suggest that this is a simple and very familiar resistance to change. We are all creatures of habit. We have our routines. We have our schedules. We have our To Do lists.

See if you can observe your inner dialog, the story you are telling yourself all day long. Question those thoughts. Where did they begin? What did you decide about yourself based on your upbringing and your life experiences?

With meditation and tapping practice - even just a little bit every day - you can tap while telling the story, to neutralize those thoughts and feelings and choose a new story of Health, Clarity, Connection, Joy, Love and Abundance.

EFT setup phrases to help you with release LIMITING BELIEFS:

While tapping the karate chop spots on the side of both hands, repeat these phrases out loud, (or use your own words).

"Even though my limiting beliefs and fears are holding me back in life, I now choose to release the past with love and acceptance."

"Even though I'm holding onto my old story, I'm willing to forgive myself and others. I love, honor and accept myself, just as I am."

Now for the phrases that focus on the issue to acknowledge and release the past - while tapping around on the body points.

"All these limiting beliefs about myself… I thought they were facts, All these limiting beliefs about others…I inherited them from my family. All these limiting beliefs… I've been repeating them over and over. I'm not good enough. I don't deserve to be loved. All these limiting beliefs…I'm ready to release them now. I accept myself even though I have all these feelings. They have felt true in the past. I

have the ability to change my beliefs. I am open and receptive. I am able to change. I am confident. I am strong. I am intelligent. I am enough. I am loved and appreciated for who I am."

Preparation for Meditation

1. **Settle yourself down in a comfortable position**, where you will not be disturbed for at least ten to twenty minutes. Shorter meditation periods are beneficial. Even just a few minutes can be helpful, however taking a bit more time for your mind and body to settle will give you great relief from stress, worry and fatigue.
2. **Sit so that your spine is long and open**, supporting yourself with cushions if necessary.
3. Take a few slow, deep breaths, **bringing the breath into your abdomen**, expanding the lungs and opening and softening the space around your heart.
4. Allow your awareness to settle down into your body, **focusing on the sensations of the breath**, wherever you feel them moving - in your belly, your nostrils or your throat.
5. Close your eyes if you like or keep your eyes open and relaxed and **lift the level of your gaze** to just above the

horizon line. This eye position quiets the primitive brain, quieting the thoughts and focuses your awareness on the frontal lobes or higher consciousness part of the brain. It also helps you to stay awake while meditating.

6. You might practice a **measured breathing technique** - inhaling for a count of seven, holding the breath for seven and exhaling for a count of seven. Repeat this several times, allowing your breath to relax into a natural rhythm. Observe the breath, without changing or controlling it.

7. **Concentration - The Hong-Sau Technique.** Notice the breath wherever you feel it moving, eventually noticing the breath at the top of the nose and bringing your attention to the spiritual eye, or sixth chakra at the point between the eyebrows. As the breath flows in, silently repeat "Hong," as the breath flows out, silently repeat "Sau." Follow the natural flow of the breath. Hong Sau means "I am Spirit" or "I am peace." You will find that as you use the mantra as a point of focus, your breath will naturally and gradually slow down on its own. Be very gentle with yourself. When you notice your mind wandering, bring your awareness back to the breath and back to the mantra.

   Practice with the mantra for two-thirds of your meditation time and then allow yourself to rest in the stillness, perhaps saying a healing prayer, affirmation or visualization.

Forgiveness Is Not An Intellectual Exercise

"Forgiveness isn't an intellectual exercise. If you attempt to mentally forgive someone who hurt or betrayed you but don't release the anger, resentment, and grief, it's like snipping off the top of a dandelion and leaving the long roots in the earth."

–Dr. Christiane Northrup

Dr. Northrup is one my very favorite authors and speakers. I've enjoyed her groundbreaking book *Women's Bodies, Women's Wisdom* since 1995.

Dr. Northrup has been bravely telling the truth to women and standing up to western medicine for many, many years.

One of her "*12 Steps For Healing*" and one of the keys to health and healing is FORGIVENESS.

She tells her healing story of being reported to the medical board for how she treated a patient. She stewed over the situation for weeks and then came to the willingness to write to the person who had reported her to acknowledge her feelings and forgive him - releasing the fear in her body. The case was dismissed.

She offers a lovely meditation from Stephen Levine that you may find helpful with forgiving yourself and others:

1. Close your eyes . . .

Reflect on the word forgiveness and what it means to you.

Very gently, allow the image of someone for whom you have resentment to come to your mind, as an image, as a feeling.

In your heart, silently say, "*I forgive you.*"

"*I forgive you for however you have caused me pain. I forgive you.*"

Speak gently to them in your heart in your own words.

Allow forgiveness. Just for a moment - allow forgiveness.

Now gently let them go with your blessing.

2. You may repeat this meditation for someone who has resentment for you and ask for forgiveness:

"*I ask for forgiveness, for whatever I may have done that caused you pain. I ask your forgiveness.*"

Allow forgiveness in. Let it be and gently let them go.

3. To complete your Forgiveness Meditation, turn to your own heart.

Say "*I forgive you (use your own name).*" Let the healing in.

Then extend the forgiveness out to all beings.

"*May all beings be forgiven, may all beings be at peace, may all beings be free.*"

Give yourself plenty of time for this practice - perhaps several days or weeks. Meditate, write in your journal, open and soften the space around your heart as you practice forgiving yourself and others.

"Releasing your old emotions and replacing them with loving kindness toward yourself is like climbing to a mountain top and breathing clean fresh air."

Rewrite Your Past, Transform Your Future

This is the subtitle of a very powerful book called *Matrix Reimprinting Using EFT* by Karl Dawson and Sasha Allenby.

I was introduced to this technique several years ago and have experienced amazing healing and witnessed healing for my clients.

Karl and Sasha were teaching EFT for many years for healing and began to utilize Bruce Lipton's work in quantum physics, Rupert Sheldrake's work with morphic fields and the research of the Heart Math Institute.

They learned from trauma specialist Dr. Robert Scaer that traumas in our young lives create a freeze response, when we are not able to fight or flee. These traumas, large and small are stored in our bodies and to our subconscious minds, they feel like current events.

The magic happens with Matrix Reimprinting when we imagine we are connecting with our younger selves that have experienced trauma. This may be big T trauma like illness or accident and it could be small t trauma like being lost in the grocery store.

Working With an EFT/ Matrix Practitioner

This type of healing work is done with an EFT practitioner and not by ourselves. It can be gentle, powerful and effective. Imagining that we are introducing ourselves to our younger self and tapping with them to provide connection and support. Once we have tapped with our younger self, we are able to re-imagine a new picture of the circumstances. It is truly a miraculous process.

If this information is intriguing to you, I recommend you open to more information. I have trained with Rob Nelson in Santa Rosa, who has trained with Karl Dawson.

I have heard so many heartening healing stories about this process, even with vets and others suffering with PTSD, when other methods have not been effective to relieve flashbacks, nightmares, depression and other symptoms of trauma.

I know that this all may sound very woo-woo and I'm happy to offer a private session to give you an experience of Matrix Reimprinting with EFT to see what is possible.

Awareness Practice

Awareness of the Breath

Often when I'm teaching someone who is new to Meditation, they will say: "I can't meditate - I can't quiet my mind." That's when I love to suggest that thinking of it as AWARENESS PRACTICE and simply focusing on the breath can be so helpful.

Meditation is not something mysterious and mystical. It is simply a technique and a tool to train our minds to stay in the present moment. Sitting quietly and focusing on the sensations of the breath can help to quiet the thoughts and calm the body and mind. Even noticing the breath throughout the day can bring us back to center and release anxiety.

Awareness of the Body Sensations

A very effective way to improve your wellbeing is to practice noticing when you feel tension and congestion in your body. Basically catching yourself in habits of physical tension and responding mindfully.

I have been noticing tension in my shoulders. I seem to accumulate tension there and catch myself often tightening those muscles throughout the day.

Every time I catch myself holding tension - I get up and jiggle, breathe, stretch - especially with arms over my head - and remind my body to relax.

Awareness of the Environment

We are all surrounded by the sounds of traffic, machinery, television and other people. Perhaps you also add music in your home, in the car or in your headphones. Do you ever simply enjoy sitting in silence? One of the most wonderful benefits of Meditation is turning our attention inward to unplug from the external world. This is very calming and allows us to listen to our own intuition and inner wisdom.

Is your living space comfortable and calming? I've been on another round of clearing clutter from my home - sorting, tossing and donating feels so satisfying and leaves me with only those things that I truly love and enjoy. Being more intentional with what I allow into my space helps me to appreciate the beauty and creativity I'm bringing into my environment.

Awareness of Self & Others

Another way to practice Mindfulness, is to pay conscious attention to how you interact with other people. Notice who you enjoy being around. Notice who drains your energy and who is fun to be with. Make conscious choices about where you put your energy and time. Allow time for your own self-care and rest. I say Yes -And. Yes - I take good care of myself - And - I enjoy time with friends and family.

Are You New To Tapping?

I know it seems crazy however this simple, effective acupressure self-healing technique will help you in so many ways - physically, emotionally and spiritually.

Begin with the **Basic Recipe** to acknowledge and release whatever is bothering you right now - physical pain, stress, anxiety or worry.

Gently tapping on the side of both hands: *"Even though I have this pain (be specific), I love and accept myself, just as I am."*

"Even though I have this persistent pain in my back, and part of me is holding on, for whatever reason, conscious or unconscious, I choose to relax and open to the healing, with love and acceptance."

While tapping around on the 10 body points: *"This pain… this persistent pain… this pain in my body…this pain…it's wearing me out. All this pain…what if I could relax, just a little bit? This pain…this pain….I'd really like to relax and let go."*

You Are Tapping & Wondering What to Say?

If you have been practicing tapping and are wondering what to say, please remember that the very best practice is to use your own words and check in between rounds - notice your thoughts, emotions and memories.

Include the new information in your next tapping round or just tap while focusing on the issue, without saying anything out loud.

You Are Getting Results & Want to Learn More?

You may have heard that I'm a big fan of the folks at The Tapping Solution. Nick Ortner's book *The Tapping Solution* and *The Tapping Solution For Pain Relief* are wonderful resources of more information about EFT.

If weight loss is one of your goals, I highly recommend Jessica Ortner's book *The Tapping Solution for Weight Loss & Body Confidence.*

Nick and Jessica (brother & sister) also have numerous videos about EFT Tapping.

Delighted With Tapping & Want to Help Others?

When I first learned about EFT years ago for pain relief, I sought out teachers in Marin and studied with them for years, until they retired from teaching. I now highly recommend my friend, Rob Nelson, in Santa Rosa for EFT classes and training.

He offers regular, reasonably priced practitioner trainings in small groups at his office in downtown Santa Rosa. Rob is a therapist who now uses only EFT in his practice, as well as training folks for their own healing and to help others. Here is his web site: www.tappingthematrix.com.

Even if you only remember to pat your heart and take a deep breath when stopping at red lights, use tapping to calm your nervous system, relieve tension and stress and bring you back to center.

Conclusion & Blessings On Your Journey

Thank you so much for joining me on this journey through the practice of Meditation and EFT tapping for healing and wellbeing.

I wish you much joy and success as you integrate these practices into your life.

Strength and courage
fill my body cells.

EFT Resources & Books

www.permissiontorelax.com My web site for resources and information.

www.eftunited.com Extensive site with workbooks, DVDs and case studies.

www.youtube.com/watch?v=aoSzivsQkVI Tap 'O the Morning with Brad Yates. Very fun!

www.tappingthematrix.com Rob Nelson's training for EFT and Matrix Reimprinting.

Coming To Our Senses **by Jon Kabat-Zinn**

Discover the Power of Meridian Tapping
by Patricia Carrington, PhD

Hacking Reality **by Rob Nelson**

Life's Companion, Journal Writing as a Spiritual Quest **by Christina Baldwin**

Matrix Reimprinting Using EFT **by Karl Dawson & Sasha Allenby**

Meditations for Caregivers **by Barry J. Jacobs, PsyD & Julie L. Mayer, PsyD**

Meditation for the Love of It **by Sally Kempton**

No Matter the Question Meditation Is the Answer **by Becca Pronchick**

Tapping Into Ultimate Success **by Jack Canfield & Pamela Bruner**

Tapping Into Wealth **by Margaret M. Lynch**

The Tapping Solution **by Nick Ortner**

The Tapping Solution for Manifesting Your Greatest Self **by Nick Ortner**

The Tapping Solution for Creating Lasting Change **by Jessica Ortner**

The Tapping Solution for Pain Relief **by Nick Ortner**

The Tapping Solution for Parent, Children & Teenagers **By Nick Ortner**

The Tapping Solution for Weight Loss & Body Confidence **by Jessica Ortner**

The Grief Recovery Handbook by **John W. James and Russell Friedman**

Wherever You Go There You Are **by Jon Kabat-Zinn**

Made in the USA
San Bernardino, CA
13 November 2019